UNDERSTANDING
BIOLOGY
THROUGH
PROBLEM
SOLVING

Blackie

UNDERSTANDING
BIOLOGY

First published 1991
© Harry Hoey 1991

Illustrated by David Gardiner
Cover photo by Frank Lane Picture Agency Ltd

Published by Blackie and Son Ltd
Bishopbriggs, Glasgow G64 2NZ
7 Leicester Place, London WC2H 7BP

British Library Cataloguing in Publication Data
Hoey, T. H.
Understanding biology—through problem solving.
1. Biology
I. Title
574

ISBN 0 216 92938 5 (without answers)
ISBN 0 216 92939 3 (with answers)

Filmset by Advanced Filmsetters (Glasgow) Ltd
Printed in Great Britain by Thomson Litho Ltd,
East Kilbride, Scotland

CONTENTS

ACKNOWLEDGEMENTS

Nature Photographers Ltd (p. 6); Stephen Power (p. 8); NSCA (p. 8); US Forest Service (p. 8); Frank Lane Picture Agency (p. 9); Reginald Kaye Ltd (p. 11); Natural History Photographic Agency (NHPA) (p. 14); Rowatt and Best (p. 18); Pan Britannica Industries Ltd (p. 23); G-P Inveresk Corporation (p. 25); Smith Kline Beecham (p. 42); WHO. Geneva (p. 47); BAA plc (p. 50); HMSO (p. 65); Scottish Milk Marketing Board (p. 73); HMSO (p. 79); MENCAP (p. 92); Severn Trent Water Authority (p. 106); Robert Gray (p. 109).

THE BIOSPHERE

1   IDENTIFICATION KEY – BIRDS

Organisms can be identified by using keys. The following table lists some of the identifiable features of seashore birds.

Feature	Seashore Birds				
	Shellduck	Oyster catcher	Greenshank	Snipe	Godwit
Feet	Webbed	Not webbed	Not webbed	Not webbed	Not webbed
Orange/red bill	Present	Present	Absent	Absent	Absent
Green legs	Absent	Absent	Present	Present	Absent
Leg length	Short	Short	Long	Short	Long

TASK

Using the information in the table, complete the branching key below.   *(3)*

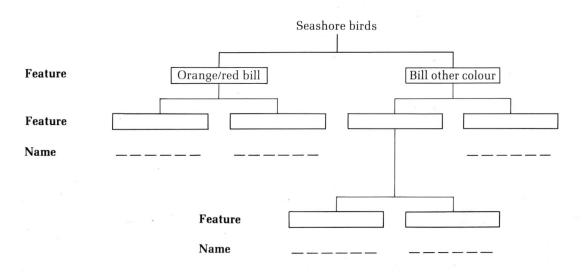

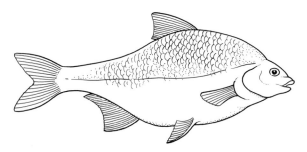

Fish with greyish fins, broad-bodied and 40–80 cm in length

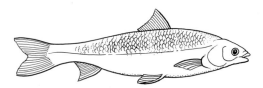

Silvery fish, thin and medium sized

TASKS

Using the key for Freshwater Fish shown opposite:
a Identify the two fish shown.   (2)
b Describe the appearance of a roach.   (2)

1 Small fish with 3 or 10 spines on the back . . . . . .   *Stickleback*
   Variable-sized fish with a normal back fin or fins . . .   **2**
2 Broad-bodied fish **3**
   Long, thin, sleek fish **7**
3 Fish with red fins **4**
   Fish without red fins **6**
4 Fish with two fins on the back and stripes down the sides . .   *Perch*
   Fish with one back fin and no stripes **5**
5 Fish with an upward-facing mouth above the central line   .   *Rudd*
   Fish with a downward-facing mouth on the central line   . .   *Roach*
6 Fish with a long fin down the back . . . .   *Carp*
   Fish with a small single fin on the centre of the back   . . .   *Bream*
7 Fish with or without a distinct pink stripe along the side and with or without spots   . . .   *Trout*
   Fish not pink and without spots **8**
8 Very large green fish with large teeth in a protruding mouth   .   *Pike*
   Not as above **9**
9 Fish with one long and one small back fin . . . . . .   *Grayling*
   Fish with a single small back fin **10**
10 Very small fish with black stripes along the sides   . . .   *Minnow*
   Medium-sized silvery fish   . .   *Dace*

3 SEAWEED

Species of seaweed are well adapted to living within a particular habitat. However, the habitat may be restricted by biotic factors, such as competition between species *or* by abiotic factors, such as tidal movements.

Narrow ranges of environmental conditions can be seen on a rocky shore due to the effects of the tide. For example, at high tide the water rises on the shore to the high tide level, then flows back out again. During periods when the tide is out or when it is not high, creatures living in this area are exposed to the air.

Seaweed	Growth range
A Spiral wrack	From very high tide to 2 m below high tide
B Bladder wrack	From high tide to 1 m below mid-tide
C Serrated wrack	From mid-tide to low tide
D Ascophyllum	From 2 m above low tide to 1 m below very low tide
E Laminaria	From very low tide to 4 m below very low tide

a Copy the graph and using the data, complete the line bar graph to show the vertical range of the seaweeds. (See example). *(1)*

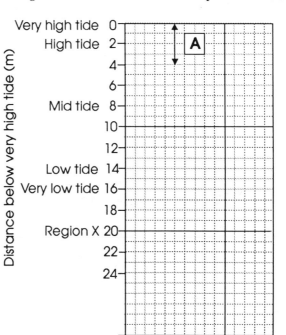

b Which species is unable to grow if exposed to the air? *(1)*
c Which *three* species do you find growing between the low tide and the mid-tide regions? *(1)*
d The lack of which environmental factor can explain the fact that plants do *not* grow below region X. *(1)*

Why fertilizers are used

The average soil does not contain enough of some of the essential nutrients to provide either a healthy crop or a satisfactory and economic yield. For this reason, soil reserves must be supplemented to meet the full demands of the crop. This is especially important at a time when plant breeders have produced new varieties with a much higher yield potential. So more nutrients are needed in the soil if this potential is to be achieved. Three of the major elements needed in the soil are nitrogen (N), phosphorus (P) and potassium (K).

Function of N, P and K in plants

Nitrogen encourages rapid growth since it is the essential element in protein and in the chlorophyll which builds up carbohydrate. If it is in short supply, plants are stunted with small pale leaves and crop yields are low. Phosphorus is involved in all the vital processes in the plant cell and is essential for the growth of roots and stems, especially in early life. A shortage leads to small roots, short stems and discoloured leaves. Potassium is involved

in many enzyme systems and in the control of carbon dioxide intake which is needed for photosynthesis and the production of carbohydrate.

Why NPK levels may be low

The reserve of nitrogen in the soil is mostly in the form of organic matter. This gradually breaks down, releasing nitrate and, if there are no active roots present at that time, some of this will be lost. Since nitrate is so readily soluble and leached, large residues cannot be accumulated. What is not taken up by the roots drains out in the water moving through the soil. In waterlogged soils, nitrogen gas may be produced and pass into the air. Phosphate and potash, on the other hand, react with other soil constituents and form compounds which may be only very slightly soluble. So it is possible to build up reserves, which may not need to be supplemented every year unless the soil is markedly deficient.

Association of Agriculture

| TASKS |

a Using the information, construct a table which shows the functions of the minerals, nitrogen, phosphorus and potassium in plants. (4)

b What *two* main reasons are given for the use of fertilizers? (2)

c Using the information on *Why NPK levels may be low*, complete the boxes in the diagram opposite. (3)

d What reason is given for the fact that phosphate and potash (potassium) are *not* so easily lost from soils by leaching? (1)

e Describe the appearance of a plant which lacks nitrogen. (1)

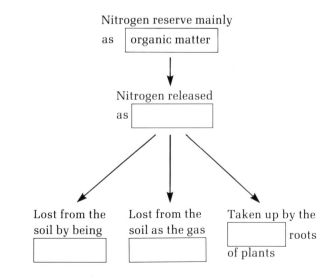

Nitrogen reserve mainly

as [organic matter]

↓

Nitrogen released

as [   ]

Lost from the soil by being [   ]

Lost from the soil as the gas [   ]

Taken up by the [   ] roots of plants

f Organic growers would disagree with the statement that nutrients *cannot be replaced fast enough by chemical processes from within the soil itself or from plant residues returned to the soil.*
Select from the list opposite those factors which an organic grower would consider as good farming practice. *(1)*

List
1 Return plant materials to the soil as compost, manure, etc
2 Spray fields with chemical fertilizers
3 Leave the field ploughed over the winter season
4 Keep the land well drained
5 Plough the field only when ready to plant the new crop.

5   WOODLAND MICE

Changes in population can occur within an ecosystem. These changes can often be related to factors within the ecosystem. The rate of change in a population of mice in a woodland area was followed over a period of two weeks.

The rate of change of a population can be calculated using the formula
$$r = (b + i) - (d + e)$$
where, in a given period of time,
r = rate of change of population
b = birth rate
d = death rate
i = immigration rate (number entering from other areas)
e = emigration rate (number leaving to other areas).

The following results were obtained for mice in a woodland area.

Birth rate	= 242 mice
Death rate	= 207 mice
Immigration rate	= 11 mice
Emigration rate	= 21 mice

TASKS

a Using the results, calculate the rate of change of the population over the two week period. *(1)*

b An increase in the rate of which *two* factors would lead to a decrease in the population. *(1)*

c One technique used in sampling was that of traps. After trapping, the mice were released back into the woodland. Explain how you would make sure that the same mouse was *not* counted twice. *(1)*

d Three months later the following results were obtained within the same woodland area.

Birth rate	= 100
Death rate	= 120
Immigration rate	= 10
Emigration rate	= 5

1 Calculate how the rate of change in population had altered during the three month period. *(1)*
2 What is the season of the year and give a reason to support your answer? *(2)*

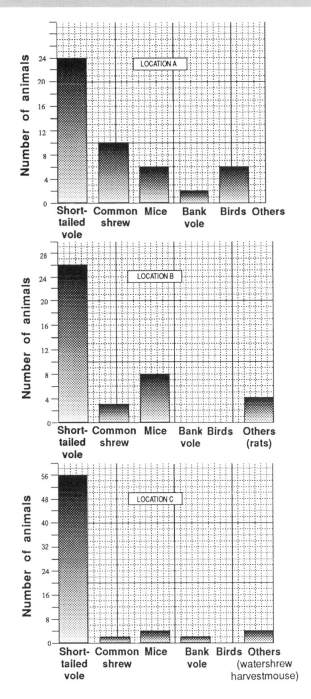

The population of barn owls has been decreasing over the past few years mainly due to changes in farming methods. Much of the research into owl populations has related to the owls' food source. This kind of study is made easier due to the fact that owls regurgitate the undigested remains of their prey as pellets.

The three bar charts show the analysis of regurgitated pellets from barn owls studied in three separate locations A, B and C.

Barn owl

TASKS

a Which animal group is the most common prey for the owls? (1)

b State the main differences in prey between locations A and B. (2)

c What is the average number of mice caught within the three locations? (1)

d Of the total number of animals found in owl pellets at location A, what percentage are short-tailed voles? (1)

e What evidence supports the statement that the owls in locations A, B and C live in habitats which differ in some way? (1)

f Name *one* of the changes in farming methods which could have affected barn owl populations. (1)

7 CFCs

Chlorofluorocarbons (CFCs) are gases which cause the ozone layer to be broken down. The ozone layer is responsible for the absorption of many of the harmful rays from the sun. These rays are known to increase the chance of skin cancer in humans. Industrial uses include CFCs being used as the gas in aerosol sprays and refrigerators, and as the means of foaming in various compounds used in packaging and soft furnishings. One of the main concerns with CFCs is that they remain active in the atmosphere for many years.

In Montreal, in September 1987, at a meeting of countries concerned about depletion of the ozone layer, an international agreement was signed, which agreed to cut back the levels of industrial emission of CFCs by 50 per cent.

The graph shows present CFC levels in the atmosphere and the projected figures of how levels could change up to the year 2100, with and without reduction in the levels of emissions.

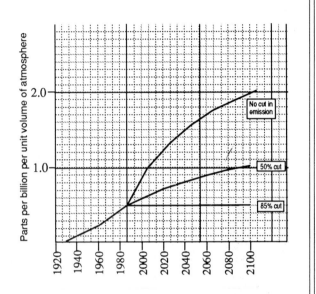

This first appeared in New Scientist magazine, London, the weekly review of Science and Technology

TASKS

a What is the main theme of the passage? *(1)*

b In which year did industrial emission of CFCs first occur? *(1)*

c What are the projected levels of increase of CFCs in the atmosphere from 1987 to 2100 (in parts per billion per unit of volume of atmosphere):
  1 with no cut in emissions
  2 with a 50% cut in emission
  3 with an 85% cut in emission? *(3)*

d Account for the fact that even if a total ban was put on the use of CFCs, they would still be present in the atmosphere for several years. *(1)*

e Account for the fact that an increase in CFC levels in the atmosphere is a danger to humans. *(2)*

f State *two* uses of CFC gases in industry. *(1)*

Pollutant gases have adverse effects on the environment. The amounts of these gases have been increasing over the years due to global activities.

Domestic smoke

Car exhaust fumes

The table below shows the source and amount of some pollutant gases produced by
1 human activities and
2 natural activities.

Volcanic eruption

Pollutant gas	Human activities		Natural activities	
	Source	Amount produced per year (millions of tonnes)	Source	Amount produced per year (millions of tonnes)
Carbon monoxide	Vehicle exhausts	300	Forest fires	3000
Sulphur dioxide	Burning coal/oil/ Industry	150	Volcanoes	10
Nitrogen oxide	Vehicle exhausts/ Burning of fuels	50	Bacterial action/ Electrical storms	160
Hydrocarbon	Vehicle exhausts/ Industry	80	Biological action	1000

a For which gases is nature the greatest source of pollution? (2)
b Which gases are produced by motor cars? (2)
c What is the ratio of the amount of carbon monoxide produced from human activity to that from natural sources? (1)

d What percentage of sulphur dioxide produced is from natural sources? (1)
e On average, how much hydrocarbon is passed into the atmosphere per month from both human and natural sources? (1)

9 ACID RAIN

The death of trees due to acid rain is related to changes in pH which are brought about in the soil.

John set up a series of experiments to investigate the effect of acid rain on seed germination. He soaked separate pieces of filter paper in solutions with a range of pH values from pH 4 to pH 8. Then he sprinkled a handful of cress seeds onto each piece of paper. The filter paper and seeds were covered with a glass dish and left for one week in the laboratory.

John's results are shown in the table.

Effect of acid rain

pH		Number of seeds which germinate
Acid	4	0
	5	10
	6	64
Neutral	7	60
	8	52
Alkali	9	8

TASKS

a Draw a bar chart to show the results. (3)
b State one way in which the method used by John could have affected the fairness of the investigation. How could this source of error be removed? (2)
c If the rain falling on an area of land over a number of years is highly acidic, predict what would be one of the effects on plant growth. (1)

10 THE GREENHOUSE EFFECT

Read the passage below and complete the tasks which follow.

Accurate measurements of the amount of carbon dioxide in the air were first taken at Mauna Loa (in Hawaii) in 1957.
These measurements are an important guide because they are taken far away from any major source of industrial pollution, and
5 represent the well-mixed¹ state of the atmosphere. They show a clear annual rhythm, associated with the seasonal changes in vegetation over the land masses of the Northern hemisphere. The Earth's vegetation "breathes" carbon dioxide in and out over an annual cycle (this is dominated by the Northern hemisphere
10 because that is where most land lies). But by the 1970's it was also clear that this annual cycle is superimposed on a rising trend of global mean carbon dioxide concentration.
In l957, the concentration of carbon dioxide in the atmosphere was 315 parts per million (ppm). It is now about 350 ppm (0.035
15 per cent). Most of the extra carbon comes from burning fossil fuel, especially coal; part of the increase may be due to the destruction of tropical forests.
The increase in the carbon dioxide concentration of the atmosphere, however, corresponds to slightly less than half the
20 amount of carbon dioxide produced by human activities each year. Roughly half the carbon dioxide we produce is absorbed in some natural sink (or sinks). Some may be taken up by vegetation, which grows more vigorously in an atmosphere enriched with carbon dioxide—"vegetation" here includes the
25 biomass of the sea, dominated by micro-organisms such as plankton. Some may be dissolved in the oceans.

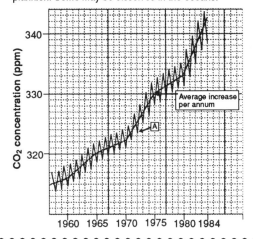

This first appeared in New Scientist

TASKS

a What is the main theme of the passage? *(1)*

b Why is it important that carbon dioxide measurements are taken from air that is in a *well-mixed* state (line 5)? *(2)*

c What season of the year is it in the Northern Hemisphere when the carbon dioxide level is at point A on the graph. *(1)*

d From the graph find how many years it took for the average annual carbon dioxide level to increase from 320 to 340 parts per million. *(1)*

e What *two* possible reasons are given for the increase in carbon dioxide levels? *(1)*

f What *two* reasons are given to explain the fact that the increase in carbon dioxide level in the atmosphere is slightly less than half the amount produced by human activities each year (lines 18–26)? *(2)*

g Using the data from lines (13 to 15), calculate the percentage increase in the carbon dioxide level from 1957. *(1)*

h Carbon dioxide in the atmosphere helps in preventing heat loss from the Earth due to radiation.
Explain the effect that the change in carbon dioxide levels has on the temperature of our planet. *(2)*

11 LICHENS

Lichens are sensitive to air pollution. For this reason, the presence or absence of certain species of lichen can be used as an indicator of the levels of air pollution.

Lichens grow on the barks of trees. Three growth forms of the lichen can be identified:
1 Crustose (powdery)
2 Foliose (leafy)
3 Fructicose (shrubby).

The graph shows the change in numbers of each lichen type with distance from a town centre. The samples were taken at random using quadrat frames.

Old Man's Beard lichen

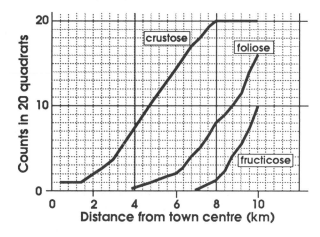

TASKS

a Which lichen form is most resistant to air pollution? *(1)*

b At what distance from the town centre do foliose types first show a count of 8 in 20 quadrat frames? *(1)*

c When fructicose types are present at a count of 5 in 20 quadrats, what is their distance from the town centre? *(1)*

d Why is a count in 20 quadrats used in each location rather than a count in a single quadrat? *(1)*

e What is the ratio of crustose to foliose types at a distance of 10 km from the town centre? *(1)*

f The quadrat samples were taken at random. Suggest how such a random sampling procedure could be carried out. *(2)*

Aluminium

Aluminium occurs naturally in some water supplies, and is also added during purification of some tap-water. Most aluminium (from either source) is taken out before it gets into the mains supply, since too much can discolour the water. There is growing evidence that high intakes of aluminium could be associated with Alzheimer's Disease (a form of senile dementia).

Lead

Large quantities of lead can damage the brain and nervous system, cause anaemia and affect the muscles. Lead gets into drinking water mainly from lead pipes, which you may find inside pre-1976 houses or connecting these houses to the water mains. In areas where they know lead is a general problem, water authorities treat water to keep levels as low as possible.

Nitrate

High levels of nitrates in tap-water can increase the risk of *methaemoglobinaemia* a very rare blood disease which can affect bottle-fed babies whose feeds are made up with tap-water (even if it's boiled first). There is also concern about the effect of nitrates on all age groups, because products which are formed when nitrates are broken down in the body have been shown to be carcinogenic in animals. So far, studies have not confirmed suggested links between nitrates and cancer in humans.

Concern about nitrates has grown in recent years because of an increase in nitrate levels in soil and water in some parts of the country. The main cause of higher nitrate levels in soil is likely to be more intensive farming which includes greater use of nitrogen fertilizers. Some of these nitrates get washed into rivers and underground water supplies and eventually find their way into tap-water.

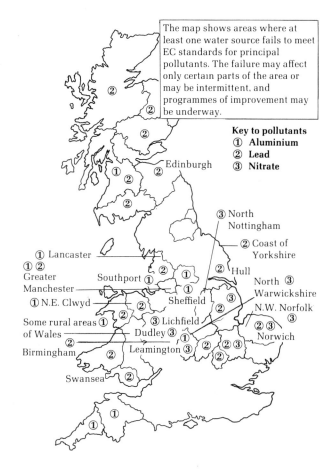

The map shows areas where at least one water source fails to meet EC standards for principal pollutants. The failure may affect only certain parts of the area or may be intermittent, and programmes of improvement may be underway.

Key to pollutants
① Aluminium
② Lead
③ Nitrate

Read the information in the article and then complete the tasks which follow:

TASKS

a Using the information on nitrates, identify *two* areas on the map where you would expect intensive farming to take place. *(1)*

b Which pollutant is most common in both Wales and Scotland? *(1)*

c Explain how nitrates find their way into tap water. *(2)*

d List *two* of the risks linked to high levels of nitrates in drinking water. *(2)*

e What action could be taken by water authorities to prevent lead from being a water pollutant? *(1)*

f Copy and complete the table below using the data on aluminium and lead. *(3)*

Pollutant	How introduced to water	Possible effect(s)
Aluminium	1 Occurs naturally 2	1
Lead	1	1 2 Causes anaemia 3

13   THE MEALYBUG

Read the passage and then complete the tasks which follow.

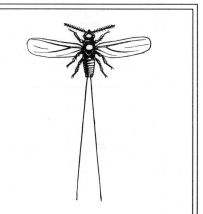

In the 1930's the coffee plantations of Kenya were invaded by an insect pest which had been accidentally introduced from Uganda. The insect pest, a mealybug, was resistant to insecticide sprays due to its waxy cuticle. It was soon discovered that in Uganda, this plant pest was kept under control using a species of parasitic insect the adult stage of which can fly. The parasite lays it's eggs inside a mealybug. When the eggs hatch the young parasites feed inside the mealybug and eventually kill it. This species of parasitic insect was released into the Kenyan coffee plantations and within three years the mealybug had been brought under control. The coffee plantations were saved using a biological control method.

TASKS

a Why did the mealybug not reach destructive levels in Uganda? *(1)*

b Why did the mealybug reach a destructive level in Kenya? *(1)*

c What reason is given for insecticides being unsuitable in the control of the pest. *(1)*

d How was the invasion by mealybugs brought under control? *(1)*

e Using the information in the text, give a definition of biological control. *(1)*

f Give *one* possible advantage of biological control methods over chemical control methods, such as the use of insecticides. *(1)*

g How does a single parasite manage to infect a large number of mealybugs? *(1)*

Attempts to reintroduce the red squirrel to England may be doomed. Zoologist Jessica Holm, who has spent five years monitoring southern England's last stronghold of reds on the Isle of Wight, believes they are inherently disadvantaged compared with the grey
5 squirrels that have replaced them throughout England.

Greys are more efficient at exploiting alternative food sources when crops fail, have a higher survival rate and can tolerate denser populations. Drastic measures would be needed to ensure the reds' survival, she says.

10 Further evidence is provided by Dr Pat Morris, of London University, who says red squirrels' numbers have been declining for centuries, not because greys have taken over but because the red squirrel's habitats, particularly woodlands, have changed. 'Coniferous woodlands, where reds do better because their food supplies last
15 longer, are mainly managed plantations, which can take 35 years to mature,' said Dr Morris.

The problem has been exacerbated by the planting of deciduous screens round conifers, giving greys—which thrive in such trees—a head start. As a result, scientists liks Jessica Holm believe
20 conservation efforts should be directed at saving isolated red colonies rather than attempting reintroduction.

However, even if the reds were completely lost, it would not be a disaster, she says. 'Conservation is only really justified in the case of the last of a particular animal. There are plenty of red squirrels on the
25 Continent.'

NICK NUTTALL

Observer

TASKS

a Why does zoologist Jessica Holm believe that attempts to *reintroduce the red squirrel may be doomed* (lines 1–5)? (1)

b State *two* ways in which greys have an advantage over reds. (2)

c It is stated that red squirrel numbers should increase in coniferous woodlands *because their food supplies last longer* (lines 13–16).

What reason is given for the fact that an increase in red squirrel numbers does not occur in a managed plantation? (2)

d Why does the scientist feel that *even if reds were completely lost, it would not be a disaster* (lines 22–25)? (1)

15

A technique used for sampling populations of organisms living in freshwater involves sweeping a net through the water at a constant speed for a fixed distance.

Students were asked to investigate the tadpole population for a pond. The pond measured 200 m² and had an average depth of 1 m. The net used had a rectangular opening of 0.1 m × 0.2 m.

The net was swept through the water at a constant speed for a fixed distance of 1 m. The volume of water sampled in each sweep can be calculated from the area of the opening and the distance moved through the water.

The students took their samples from around the edges of the pond as they had no waders or boat. The number of tadpoles in each net sample was counted and the results are given here.

Sample number	1	2	3	4	5	6	7	8	9	10
Number of tadpoles	20	12	32	0	4	8	4	8	12	20

TASKS

a Using the results, estimate the following:
  1 the average number of tadpoles per sample *(1)*
  2 the average number of tadpoles per m³ *(1)*
  3 the total number of tadpoles in the pond. *(1)*
b State how the sampling method used by the students affects the fairness of the investigation and how this source of error could be removed. *(2)*

16

A study was carried out to measure the mouse population in a field.

Small mammal traps were used and 200 mice were captured. These mice were tagged with a metal number and released. The tagged mice were then free to mix with the rest of the population.

A week later 120 mice were captured from the same area. Of these, only 12 mice carried a metal tag.

TASKS

a Using the following formula, estimate the total population of mice in the field.

$$\frac{X}{A} = \frac{B}{C}$$

  where:
  X = total population
  A = total number tagged in 1st sample
  B = total number in 2nd sample
  C = number of tagged mice in 2nd sample *(1)*
b Suggest *two* reasons why the estimated population may differ from the actual population. *(2)*

The table below shows the features of rocky shore animals which possess a shell.

Using the information, construct a paired statement key. *(3)*

Organism	Attachment	Number of parts of shell	Shape of shell
Mussel	Threads	2	Oval
Barnacle	Cemented	6	Cone
Limpet	Suction	1	Cone
Dogwhelk	Suction	1	Helical coil
Spirorbis	Cemented	1	Coiled tube

Insecticides, which are used to control insect pests in the environment, gradually enter into the natural food chain. The level of insecticide residue present in the tissues of an organism is related to the organism's position in the food chain. The further up the food chain an organism is, the greater the level of insecticide residue present. High levels of insecticide can have harmful effects on the organism.

Bird	Concentration of insecticide (ppm)
Wood pigeon	0.8
Barn owl	3.2
Sparrow hawk	4.0
Grebe	6.0
Heron	12.8

The table shows the results of analysing the breast muscle of various birds for insecticide residues. Concentrations are in parts per million (ppm).

a Draw a bar chart to show the concentrations of insecticides in each bird. *(3)*

b What explanation, related to position in the food chain, would account for the levels present in the wood pigeon? (*Hint:* The wood pigeon feeds mainly on seeds.) *(1)*

c The heron feeds on fish, and can often be the fourth organism in a food chain. Explain why the heron is at greatest risk from insecticide residues. *(2)*

Two abiotic factors which can affect organisms living in fresh water are oxygen level and water temperature.

Graph A shows how the oxygen uptake of a fish changes with changing water temperature.

Graph B shows how the level of dissolved oxygen changes with changing water temperature.

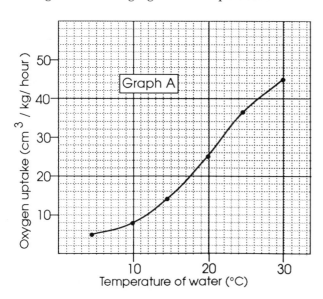

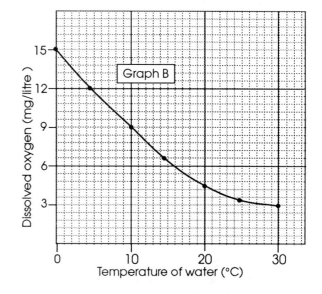

TASKS

a By how much does the oxygen uptake of a fish increase when the temperature increases from 4.5 °C to 25.5 °C? *(1)*

b A factory uses river water at 4.5 °C as a coolant. On one occasion the water discharged back into the river was at 30 °C.

  1 Calculate the percentage change in the level of dissolved oxygen between the river water at 4.5 °C and the discharged water at 30 °C. *(1)*

  2 Using the data from both graphs, explain the fact that, after this discharge, fish were seen dying downstream of the factory. *(2)*

c Using graph A, calculate the volume of oxygen taken up by a 2 kg fish over a 5 hour period when the water temperature is 20 °C. *(1)*

d Express as a ratio the difference in the level of dissolved oxygen at 4.5 °C and at 30 °C. *(1)*

e Using the information in graph B, calculate the mass of oxygen dissolved in 10 litres of water at a temperature of 20 °C. *(1)*

The table shows the changes in water temperature in the river from the point of discharge of the heated water from the factory.

Distance from discharge (m)	Temperature (°C)
0	20.0
10	15.0
20	12.0
30	10.0
40	8.0
50	7.5
60	6.5
70	6.0
80	5.5
90	5.0
100	5.0

Effluent discharge into river

TASKS

a Using suitable scales, plot the results as a line graph. *(3)*

b At what distance from the discharge is the elevated water temperature
  1 reduced by half *(1)*
  2 returned to the original temperature of the river? *(1)*

c Calculate the average decrease in water temperature per metre over the first 40 m from the point of discharge. *(1)*

New Scientist

The strange death of Europe's trees

Bernhard Ulrich is a quiet elfin man, a soil biologist who has spent 20 years measuring the biochemistry of soils in the Solling Forest in West Germany. Five years ago, he transformed German politics when he told *Der Spiegel,* the Country's leading news magazine, of his fears that his country's trees were dying.

The data on the opposite page shows the changes in the health of fir and spruce trees in the Black Forest over a three year period.

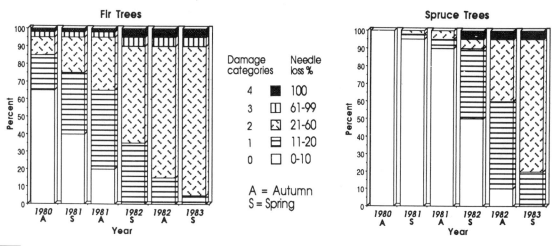

Fir Trees

Spruce Trees

Damage categories	Needle loss %
4 ■	100
3 ⊞	61-99
2 ▨	21-60
1 ☰	11-20
0 ☐	0-10

A = Autumn
S = Spring

TASKS

a What information supports the statement that spruce trees are more resistant to the effects of acid rain than fir trees? *(1)*

b By what percentage did damaged trees (categories 1–4) increase, between:
  1 spring 1981 and autumn 1981 in fir
  2 autumn 1981 and spring 1982 in spruce? *(1)*

c What percentage of fir trees were still healthy in autumn 1980? *(1)*

d If the number of spruce trees in the area originally was 10 000, calculate the number of trees at damage category 2 by autumn 1982. *(1)*

20B

The data represents a survey in 1985 of a forest in Germany affected by acid rain.

TASKS

a Using a ratio, compare each category of damage among the fir trees. *(1)*

b If there were 1200 oak trees in the forest, what would be the number of undamaged oak trees? *(1)*

c Overall, is the percentage of damaged trees greater or less than the percentage of undamaged trees? *(1)*

d What should the response of Government be to the results of the survey? *(1)*

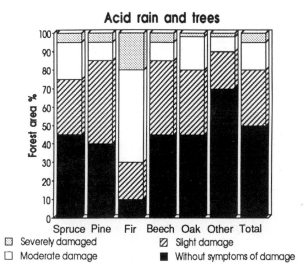

Acid rain and trees

Spruce Pine Fir Beech Oak Other Total

☒ Severely damaged
☐ Moderate damage
▨ Slight damage
■ Without symptoms of damage

19

TESTS ON FLY KILLERS

We based our tests on a British Standard method, using each killer on 1000 ordinary house flies released into a test room. We measured how quickly the flies were knocked down, and how efficiently they were killed.

GOOD VALUE   Vapona Fly Killer (79p)

KEY

Active ingredients

A = pyrethroids	G = pyrethrins
B = diazinon	H = tetramethrin
C = permethrin	I = lindane
D = bioallethrin	J = fenitrothion
E = dichlorvos	K = glue
F = pirimiphos-methyl	

	Price £	Active ingredients	Propellant	Knock-down time	Efficiency of killing
AEROSOLS					
Big D Fly and Wasp Killer	0.69	HI	H	1	4
Kybosh	1.99	CG	H	1	4
Rentokil Fly and Wasp Killer	1.45	A	H	1	4
Rentokil Insectrol	2.95	AB	C(a)	1	4
Scram Flying Insect Killer	1.20	A	C	1	4
Secto Rapid Action Fly Killer	1.09	A	C(a)	1	3
Secto Superfast Fly Killer	1.35	AE	C(a)	1	4
Vapona Fly Killer	0.79	CD	H	1	3
FLY PAPER					
Rentokil Fly Paper	0.90	K		(b)	4
ELECTRIC KILLERS					
Home Guard Indoor Unit	69.00	Electricity		(c)	3
Odell Bug Killer	25.00	Electricity		(d)	3

Propellants
C = chlorofluorocarbon
H = hydrocarbon

Knock-down time
1 = 90% of flies knocked down in 10 mins

Efficiency of killing
3 = flies died instantly
4 = flies took longer to die

(a) Use of CFC propellant under review
(b) 17% trapped after 1 hr, 89% after 24 hrs
(c) 2% killed after 1 hr, 32% after 24 hrs
(d) 3% killed after 1 hr, 36% after 24 hrs

Which? magazine

TASKS

a Using the table of results, give reasons to explain why Vapona Fly Killer is selected as *GOOD VALUE*. (1)

b Using the data for knock-down time, on the basis that 1000 flies are used in the tests, calculate:
1 the number of flies killed by Odell Bug Killer after 24 hours (1)
2 the difference between the numbers caught in Home Guard Indoor Unit and Rentokil Fly Paper after 24 hours. (1)

c Chlorofluorocarbon gases add to the breakdown of the ozone layer in the atmosphere and are viewed as pollutants. Which aerosols would *not* be recommended by conservationists? (1)

d Which of the active ingredients is used most commonly in aerosols? (1)

e Give a reason why some manufacturers use a mixture of two active ingredients rather than a single ingredient. (1)

f The British Standard Method was used in the tests.
1 What is the significance of the fact that 1000 flies are used in each test? (1)
2 Name *two* other experimental factors which would be kept constant to ensure that the results obtained with aerosols allow a fair comparison. (2)

Read the passage below and complete the tasks which follow.

Dutch scientists have identified the disease in dogs called distemper as the killer virus which is wiping out thousands of seals in the Baltic and North Seas. The scientists say more seals will die in the coming years and although the virus is the primary cause of death, 5 high levels of pollution have played an important part in the swift impact of the disease. In 1987 at the Scientific Conference on the North Sea, a report stated that certain types of algae had increased in number in coastal waters. In one incident the algae were described as a massive blanket, which was suffocating the sea life. 10 The report added that high levels of PCBs (extremely persistent and highly toxic chemicals) had been found in seals. Poisoned plankton, such as algae and microscopic animals, are eaten by little fish, which are eaten by bigger fish, which are eaten by seals. All the way up the food chain, the toxins become more concentrated. 15 Animals such as seals are at the top of the food chain. Many of these toxic PCBs are highly soluble in blubber.

Seals, therefore, tend to accumulate these compounds. The toxins are then released into the bloodstream at times of stress, for example when the seals have a high energy demand. Therefore 20 during the breeding season and during moulting the seals can have very high levels of these toxic compounds circulating in their blood. Rivers are the source of most nitrate and phosphate pollutants found in the sea. Water pollution from metals seems to fall from the air. Much of this air pollution comes from Britain, as the 25 prevailing wind blows from *The West*. Britain is particularly lucky because the currents of the North sea sweep the pollutants away from its shores towards the coast of Europe. For this reason, Britain has not been as keen to clear up the seas as its European neighbours. For example, Britain is the only country to dump 30 sewage sludge at sea.

Seal Killer Virus is Canine Distemper

Dutch scientists have identified the dog's disease, distemper, as the killer virus which is wiping out thousands of Seals in the Baltic and North Seas.

Glasgow Herald

MAN POLLUTES
SEALS PERISH

Catastrophe is a large word and one not to be used lightly. Yet the North and Baltic Seas appear to be suffering a catastrophic and wilful man-made carnage which threatens not only all marine life, but ultimately people too.

Guardian

TASKS

a The statement that seal deaths were due to a killer virus is only partially true. Why (lines 3–6)? (1)

b Explain how the massive blanket of algae suffocates sea life (lines 8–9). (2)

c What *two* reasons could explain the high levels of PCBs in seal blubber (lines 10–16). (2)

d Explain why being *extremely persistent* makes highly toxic chemicals such as PCBs dangerous to living things (line 10). (2)

e Explain why scientists think that the effects of PCBs are greatest *at times of stress* (line 18). (2)

f Our European neighbours feel that *Britain has been less keen to clear up the seas*. What fact would support this view (line 28)? (1)

g Which *two* factors make Britain *particularly lucky* with regard to pollution in the North Sea (lines 23–27)? (1)

Feeding relationships can be observed between animals and plants in a grassland habitat. Rabbits eat grass leaves and will dig for plant roots. Earthworms eat plant roots and will also pull dead leaves into their burrows. Earthworms are food for many organisms including hawks and frogs. Insects, such as moths, which feed off the nectar of flowers, are food for spiders and both in turn are food for frogs.

Many birds such as wagtails are versatile eaters and their diet includes seeds, moths and spiders. At the top of the food web are hawks and foxes and their main food sources are small vertebrates such as birds, frogs and rabbits.

TASKS

a Copy out the food web below to show the feeding relationship of the organisms and
  1 Write the name of the missing organisms into the appropriate boxes. *(3)*
  2 Insert arrows to show the *three* missing feeding relationships. *(2)*

b What is the advantage of being a versatile eater such as the wagtail? *(1)*

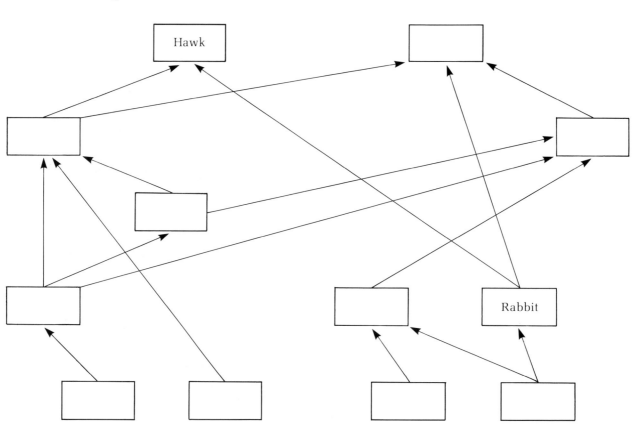

THE WORLD OF PLANTS

1 FERTILIZER

Read the passage below and complete the tasks which follow.

GOODNESS FOR GROWTH

Plants, like all living things, require a balanced diet for healthy growth. The better the diet the better they will perform.

Plants cannot grow successfully just by absorbing water through their roots. To produce stems, leaves, flowers and fruit, plants also
5 need to absorb other elements.

The main elements for plant growth include oxygen, hydrogen and carbon obtained from the air and from water. Plants also need other elements, or nutrients as they are called. The three most important are nitrogen, phosphorus and potassium, but there is a list
10 of other minerals which are also needed in very small quantities. These nutrients are often not available in the soil in sufficient quantities to encourage healthy plant growth but they can be added in the form of a fertilizer.

THE BENEFITS OF FERTILIZER

Fertilizer provides the nourishment plants need to produce strong
15 root systems, healthy leaf growth and abundant flowers and fruit. With correct feeding, bedding plants and other flowers will produce more blooms over a longer period. Well-fed vegetables will produce bigger crops with more flavour and fruit trees and
20 bushes will retain more fruit for harvest. Lawns will be greener, denser and more attractive. Well-fed plants are also more able to resist drought and attacks by disease.

Each group of plants needs different amounts of major fertilizer elements nitrogen, phosphorous and potassium. That is why you
25 will find fertilizers in various forms on the shelves of garden shops and garden centres.

If you apply the right fertilizer at the right time of year and at the right rate you will encourage optimum growth. Too little will give poor results. Too much will scorch plants. However, it is worth re-membering that fertilizers will not work miracles. They cannot
30 cure the influence of bad weather or rectify cultural faults. Neither can they produce quality crops from third rate seed or over-crowded plants.

Fertilizer Manufacturers Association

TASKS

a What reason is given for the fact that fertilizers will be found *in various forms* (lines 22–25)? *(1)*

b What is meant by the fact that fertilizers cannot *rectify cultural faults* (line 30)? *(1)*

c Give *two* of the benefits, claimed for the use of fertilizers. *(2)*

d Apart from using fertilizers and first class seeds, select *two* factors suggested in the last paragraph which would increase the chance of producing quality crops. *(2)*

e Other than the elements present in ferti-lizer, plants require *three* other main elements. Using the information in *Goodness For Growth*, construct a table which names these elements and gives each a source. *(3)*

f Other than supplying nitrogen, phos-phorus and potassium, what other argu-ment is used in paragraph 3, to support the use of fertilizers? *(2)*

2A PAPERMAKING

Read the passage below and complete the tasks which follow.

Where Britain's wood pulp comes from and, inset, the different sorts of paper that the country's mills produce (all figures are in thousand tonnes).

Papermaking is a simple process . The papermakers suspend plant fibres in water and then drain them through a sieve. The mesh traps the fibres. When the fibres dry out they become a sheet of paper. This process has not changed
5 since the first sheet of paper was produced in China, around 200BC.
These early papers were made almost wholly from hemp

(*Cannabis sativa*). When the technique spread to the West, papermakers used a mixture of hemp and linen. Hemp was
10 gradually replaced with cheap cotton from the textile industry . The paper industry also tried straw and esparto grass as alternatives, but the breakthrough came with the use of wood .

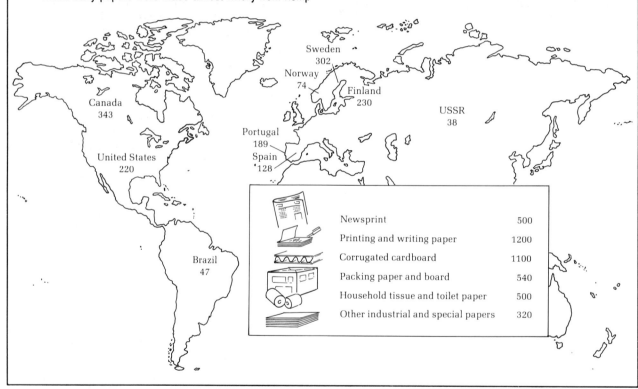

Newsprint	500
Printing and writing paper	1200
Corrugated cardboard	1100
Packing paper and board	540
Household tissue and toilet paper	500
Other industrial and special papers	320

Sweden 302
Norway 74
Finland 230
USSR 38
Canada 343
Portugal 189
Spain 128
United States 220
Brazil 47

TASKS

a What is the total tonnage of wood pulp imported into Britain? *(1)*

b Construct a bar chart to show the total production of the different sorts of paper. *(3)*

c Name *three* plant materials which can be used for papermaking (lines 7–13). *(1)*

d Describe, in your own words, the stages of paper making outlined in the passage. *(2)*

Water pollution has long been one of the paper industry's problems. Chemical processing requires between 100,000 and 300,000 litres of water for every tonne of paper. A clean and plentiful supply of water is therefore essential for papermaking. Stricter environmental controls mean that the industry has reduced the amount of pollution resulting from chemical processing of wood pulp. Paper mills now remove and reuse most of the chemicals from the effluent before discharging it. However, the bleaches that are used to whiten the paper, still pose considerable pollution problems. The bleaches are one of three types, chlorine, hydrogen peroxide and sulphur dioxide. The paper mills neutralise and dilute these effluents before discharging them into the river. Although the chief effect of stricter environmental control has been to make the industry reduce its pollution, there has been some tendency to divert the problems of pollution to underdeveloped countries, where controls, are more lax. In Sweden, one paper mill was unable to produce a particular high grade of pulp because the resulting effluent contravened the national pollution regulations. Rather than meet these strict standards the company moved its mill to Brazil.

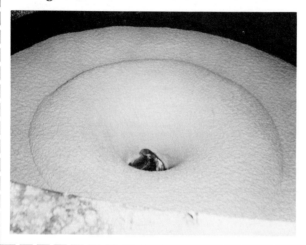

A hydropulper at Caldwells Paper Mill, Inverkeithing, Fife

TASKS

a Why are unpolluted rivers used as the location for paper mills? (2)

b Identify *two* problems of pollution which arise during the papermaking process. (2)

c The papermaking industry has responded in different ways to overcome the pollution problems. Identify:
   1 an acceptable, and
   2 an unacceptable method by which companies deal with the problem of pollution. (2)

3 CROPS AND SELF-SUFFICIENCY

Table 1 below shows some of the farm crops produced in Britain and the degree of self-sufficiency. Total self-sufficiency (100%) means that enough of a particular crop is grown to meet the needs of the country and no more has to be imported.

Table 1

Farm crops		1970	1980	1986	1987
Wheat	production*	4169	8472	13 911	12 011
	self-sufficiency %	44	88	120	131
Barley	production	7411	10 326	10 014	9219
	self-sufficiency %	90	116	162	142
Rape for oil seed	production	8	300	951	1318
	self-sufficiency %	13	69	133	108
Sugar	production	939	1106	1318	1200
	self-sufficiency %	33	47	55	57
Potatoes	production	7482	7110	6447	6595
	self-sufficiency %	92	92	88	86
Hops	production	12	10	5	5
	self-sufficiency %	97	126	86	78

Note * production in '000 tonnes

Table 2 shows the average yields in tonnes per hectare of some farm crops.

Table 2

Average yields	1970	1980	1986
	(tonnes/hectare)		
Wheat	4.2	5.9	7.0
Barley	3.4	4.4	5.2
Rape for oil seed	1.9	3.3	3.2
Sugar beet	34.1	35.1	40.4
Potatoes	27.6	34.5	36.0

TASKS

a Name the crops, in which Britain was *not* fully self-sufficient in 1970, but which were being produced in surplus by 1987. *(1)*

b Which farm crops show:
   1 the greatest percentage decrease in terms of self-sufficiency *(1)*
   2 the greatest decrease in production in tonnes? *(1)*

c How would the self-sufficiency percentage of a crop such as potatoes be calculated? *(1)*

d By what percentage does the average yield per hectare of wheat increase between 1970 and 1986? *(1)*

e Which crop shows the largest increase in tonnes per hectare between 1970 and 1986? *(1)*

f How would the average yield for a crop such as sugarbeet be calculated? *(1)*

g Construct a bar chart to show the average yields for 1986. *(3)*

4 ROOT TIP GROWTH

An investigation was carried out on the growth of the root tip of a broad bean, as follows:

1 The root was marked every 1 mm with Indian ink starting from the tip

2 The change in length of one of the 1 mm segments was recorded each day

3 The results are shown in the graph and diagrams.

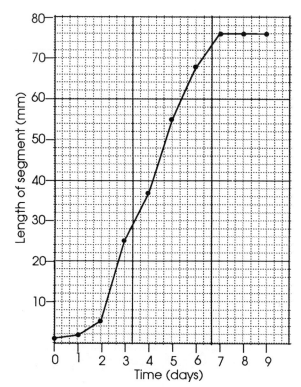

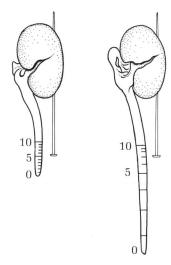

TASKS

a How many days does it take before the segment
   1 reaches its maximum length *(1)*
   2 grows to 50% of its maximum length? *(1)*

b During which day does the greatest rate of growth in length occur? *(1)*

c From the diagram, identify the area of the root tip which shows the greatest growth in length. *(1)*

d Given that bamboo shoots can grow at 0.3 mm per minute, calculate the increase in the length of a bamboo shoot over a 10 hour period of sustained growth. *(1)*

5 MAIZE OIL

The amount of oil present in maize grains can vary considerably.

An experiment was carried out in which grains were selected and measured for their oil content. Only grains with either high or low oil content were planted. When these had grown the selection process was repeated on the new grains and the oil content of each grain was measured. The graph shows the effect of selection on grains of high and low oil content over fifty generations.

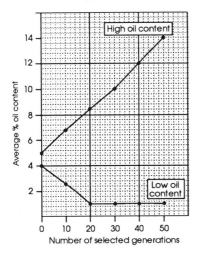

TASKS

a Many cooking oils contain a high percentage of maize oil.
How could the above experiment help cooking oil manufacturers? *(1)*

b How many generations did it take for the oil content to double in those grains selected for their high oil content? *(1)*

c How many generations did it take for the oil content to halve in those grains selected for their low oil content? *(1)*

d Calculate the difference in the average percentage oil content between the two selected strains of maize after 40 generations. *(1)*

e Given that a maize grain has an average mass of 0.4 g, calculate the average mass of oil in the strain selected for high oil content, after 50 generations. *(1)*

6 TRANSPIRATION

Water evaporates into the air spaces of a leaf from the leaf cells. The water vapour then passes out through pores (stomata) in the leaf surface. The two cells which form the stomatal pore can move apart or come together, opening and closing the pore (see diagram).

The rate of loss of water from the leaves can be measured by weighing a plant at hourly intervals.

An investigation was carried out to study the effect of light intensity on the opening and closing of the stomatal pores.

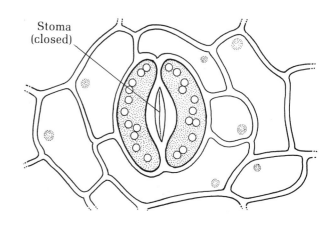

Stoma (closed)

The procedure was carried out as follows:

1 Apparatus A was used to measure the rate of water loss from the leaves at several light intensities

Apparatus A

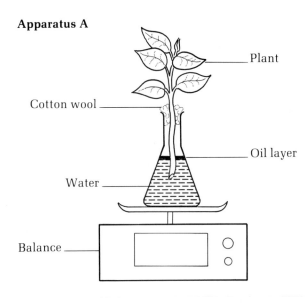

2 Apparatus B was used to measure water loss through a porous pot during the same period

Apparatus B

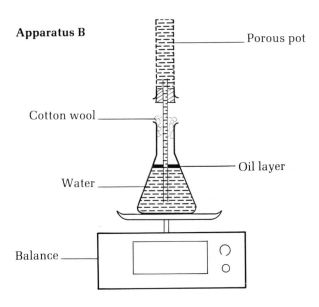

3 At each light intensity the apparatus was left for 15 minutes before starting the measurements

4 The water loss was recorded in the dark and at four different light intensities. The results are shown in the table.

Apparatus	Loss of water (g/hour)				
	Light intensity (kilolux)				
	0	10	20	30	40
A	1	15	20	22	22
B	20	20	20	20	20

TASKS

a Plot a line graph of water loss from the plant against increasing light intensity. (3)

b State the relationship between light intensity and water loss, as seen in the plant. (1)

c What evidence supports the statement that the stomata are fully open at a light intensity of 30 kilolux? (1)

d How do the results from apparatus B allow you to conclude that other environmental factors remain unchanged during the period of experimental investigation? (1)

e Predict what would be the effect on the results if the investigation is carried out at a lower temperature. Account for your prediction. (2)

f Why is the apparatus left for 15 minutes at each new light intensity before starting the measurements? (1)

g Explain why there must be an oil layer over the water surface in the flasks. (1)

h Without modifying the apparatus, how could you improve the reliability of the results obtained at each light intensity? (1)

Read the passage below and complete the tasks which follow.

Observer

Loo paper sets several green warning lights flashing. Number 1 is the chlorine-bleaching process which virtually all paper goes through. Each year thousands of
5 tonnes of chlorinated compounds (including the highly toxic dioxin) are discharged into rivers and the sea, contaminating water and killing fish. (Trace amounts of dioxins have now been found
10 left behind in paper products as a result of the bleaching, but they are unlikely to constitute a health hazard in loo paper). Although white paper is not more biodegradable than coloured, it *is* slightly
15 Greener, since colour involves bleaching and dyeing pulp, producing yet more effluence.
The other big issue is that of waste—wasted trees, wasted pulp, wasted energy. Huge
20 areas of natural forest in the USA, Canada and Northern Europe are being devastated.

Though land is replanted, the cycle may not be inexhaustible and, in any case, wildlife suffers. Since loo paper exists to be
25 chucked away, it seems madness to use top quality pulp from new trees. Loo paper is a prime candidate for recycled paper. So, look for 100 per cent recycled paper that is unbleached, or bleached by the safe
30 oxygen method. Britain is still way behind the Continent on such matters, but changes are afoot.
Traidcraft were first with a good-quality environment friendly loo paper from the
35 Mail Order Dept, Kingsway, Gateshead NE11 ONE (091491 0591). Sainsbury's Revive made from non-chlorine- bleached 100 per cent recycled waste paper, costs 59p for two rolls of 320 sheets (as against
40 Sainsbury's own-brand economy, 55p for two rolls of 240 sheets) and it's actually softer and whiter than many economy rolls.

TASKS

a What is the main theme of the passage? (1)

b Which *two* issues cause environmentalists to be concerned about the toilet paper industry (lines 2–21)? (2)

c Why is white paper viewed as *slightly Greener* than coloured toilet paper (lines 13–17)? (1)

d Explain clearly what the author means by the phrase *green warning lights flashing* (line 1). (1)

e How could manufacturers bleach paper without using chlorine (lines 28–30)? (1)

f What action, suggested by the writer, would reduce the amount of *wasted trees, wasted pulp and wasted energy* which occurs (lines 24–27)? (1)

g What counter argument does the writer put forward to those who argue that the land in natural forests is replanted and will be replaced with time (lines 22–24)? (2)

h In terms of cost per sheet which of the two named brands of toilet paper is the better buy (lines 36–42)? (1)

8 STOMATA

The table below shows the size and distribution of stomata on the leaves of various plant species. Size is expressed as the length times the breadth of a fully open stoma. Spacing is the average distance between neighbouring stomata.

Species	Average stomatal number per cm²		Average size (μm)	Spacing on lower epidermis (μm)
	Upper epidermis	Lower epidermis		
Bean	4000	28 000	7×3	67.5
Ivy	0	15 800	11×4	90.0
Maize	5200	6800	19×5	137
Tomato	1200	13 000	13×6	99.2
Wheat	3300	1400	18×7	302
Sunflower	8500	15 600	38×7	90.5
Oat	2500	2300	38×8	235.8
Geranium	1900	5900	24×9	146.0
Wandering sailor	0	1400	31×12	302

Note: *1 micrometre (μm) = 1/1000th of a millimetre (mm)

TASKS

a Describe how the average number of stomata per cm² could be calculated. (2)

b Express as a ratio the difference in the number of stomata on the upper surface of the bean to that on the lower surface. (1)

c Which plant shows the most even stomatal distribution between both leaf surfaces? (1)

d A pupil wishes to observe the structure of stomata under a microscope. The microscope available can magnify only to low power ($\times 10$). Which plant would be best for stomatal observation?
Explain your choice. (2)

e A geranium leaf was found to have a lower surface area of 15 cm² and an upper of 15 cm². Using the average stomatal numbers given in the table calculate the total number of stomata present on the leaf. (1)

f Dicotyledonous plants generally have an uneven distribution of stomata with more being present on the lower surface.
How does this statement support the fact that wheat is not a dicotyledonous plant? (1)

g What evidence supports the fact that the Wandering sailor has leaves which are designed for reducing water loss? (1)

9 PHOTOSYNTHESIS

In variegated leaves, some areas are green due to the presence of chlorophyll and others are white due to the lack of chlorophyll.

An investigation was carried out to determine if chlorophyll is required for photosynthesis to occur in plants. The ability to produce starch in the light shows that photosynthesis has taken place.

The investigation was carried out as follows:

1 A variegated geranium plant was left in the dark for 4 days to destarch the leaves of the plant
2 The plant was then left in the light for 4 hours
3 A leaf was removed and a drawing of it was made to show the distribution of green and white areas (Fig. 1)

Figure 1 Before

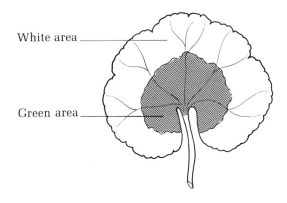

4 The leaf was tested for the presence of starch
5 After the addition of iodine solution a second drawing of the leaf was made to show the distribution of blue–black and brown areas of the leaf (Fig. 2).

Figure 2 After

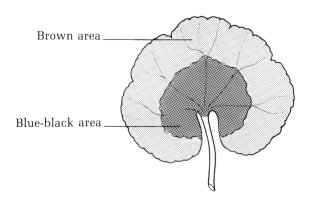

TASKS

a Why after step **1**, should a leaf have been tested for the presence of starch before exposing the plant to light in step **2**? *(2)*
b The strength of the blue–black colour, indicating the presence of starch, was poorly developed in the leaf tested. How could the procedure be altered to obtain a stronger blue–black colour? *(1)*
c What conclusion can be drawn from the results obtained? *(1)*
d Occasionally, seeds are produced which on germination have colourless leaves. Predict, with an explanation, what would happen to these seedlings. *(2)*
e Make a drawing of a leaf from its description.
  The leaf measures 5 cm at its widest. The leaf is heart-shaped and the leaf stalk arises at the V of the heart. The edges of the leaf have a saw-edged appearance, the teeth of which are small in size. *(2)*

An investigation was carried out to find the effect on growth of grass of the following:

- fertilizer
- insecticide
- a mixture of fertilizer and insecticide.

The procedure was carried out as follows
1 An area of well established lawn was marked out. The grass was mown to a height of 2 cm
2 Four strips (5 m long and 1 m wide) were marked out 1 m apart as shown

3 Each strip was treated separately as shown in the table
4 After 10 days each strip was mown again to a height of 2 cm
5 The grass cuttings were gathered and completely dried in an oven before being weighed. The dry mass results are shown in the table.

Strip	Treatment	Dry mass
1	Watered with 10 litres distilled water	700 g
2	Watered with 10 litres fertilizer solution	705 g
3	Watered with 10 litres insecticide solution	850 g
4	Watered with 10 litres fertilizer and insecticide	900 g

TASKS

a Why is it important to mow the grass in the way described in the investigation? *(1)*

b What is the purpose of treating strip 1 as described? *(1)*

c One suggestion for the result obtained in strip 3 is that better root growth has taken place. How might the treatment have led to better root growth? *(1)*

d One suggestion for the result obtained in strip 4 is that as a result of better root growth the rate of fertilizer uptake is increased.
How does the result from strip 2 support this suggestion? *(2)*

Plant growth substances affect the development of plant structures. The following graph shows the effects of different concentrations of a growth substance (auxin) on the growth of roots, stems and flowers.

The results were recorded as promotion or inhibition of growth. This was obtained by comparing the growth of the roots, stems and flowers with untreated controls.

TASKS

a What range of growth substance concentration *promotes* growth in
1 roots
2 stems? (2)

b What growth substance concentration *promotes* growth to the greatest extent in
1 flowers
2 stems? (2)

c What range of growth substance concentration *promotes* stem growth but *inhibits* root growth? (1)

d Predict what would be the effect of a solution of 10^{-7} molar growth substance on the growth of a germinating seed. (1)

e If the growth of the untreated control in the root experiment was 10 mm, what would you predict the growth of the root to be, at a growth substance concentration of 10^{-10} molar? (1)

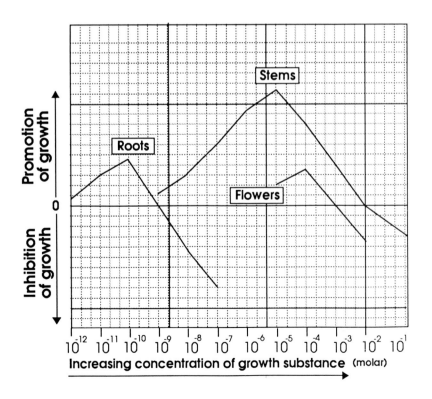

The diagrams represent sections through three leaves of a silver birch tree, (*Fagus silvatica*), and are drawn to the same scale.

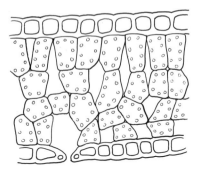

B

B—A leaf situated in the lower branches and slightly shaded by branches above

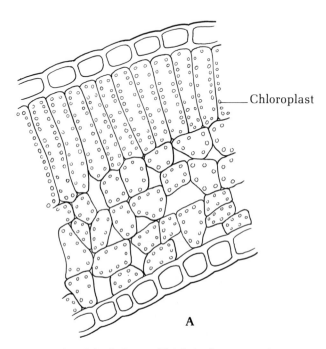

———Chloroplast

A

A—A leaf situated high in the tree and exposed to full sunlight

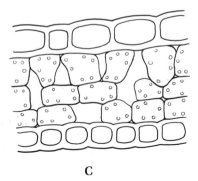

C

C—A leaf situated in the lowest branches and fully shaded by branches above

---

TASKS

a Give *two* differences in the growth response between leaves which develop in full light and leaves which develop in full shade. (2)

b Explain how each of the differences effects the photosynthetic efficiency of the leaf. (2)

BREAD WITHOUT WHEAT

Many millions of people in developing countries have abandoned staple foods prepared from traditional crops, such as sorghum and millet for white bread made with wheat. The change to wheat can upset a country's economy.
5 Urban populations are usually the first to favour wheat and the demand for traditional staples declines.

Farmers faced with declining incomes from their crops struggle to increase yields and production. Often, their efforts serve only to worsen the glut, depressing prices
10 further. Eventually, production other than for simple subsistence declines. This undermines the agricultural base on which the economy of many developing countries depends.

Bread bought in a market or shop supplants traditional
15 foods because it needs no preparation before it is eaten. Other staples, such as cassava require laborious and time-consuming preparation before cooking. Cooking can take a long time and storage life is brief.

The Food and Agriculture Organization of the United
20 Nations (FAO) has been investigating the possibility of making breads based on local starchy foodstuffs. If the people want to eat **bread**, then let them—but it should be bread free of the imported wheat.

Tropical countries could grow wheat themselves but wheat
25 grows poorly there and most local crops produce larger yields (see barchart). They also withstand the extremes of the tropical climate much better. Local crops usually require fewer and cheaper inputs such as fertilizer. Traditional staples can make a good bread if a baker adds

30 a substitute for gluten to the flour, but in nearly every case the substitute has to be imported. At the FAO we replaced gluten with xanthan gum. A species of bacteria, *Xanthomonas campestris* ferments carbohydrates to produce xanthan gum, a water-soluble polymer with a high viscosity. Although
35 expensive to buy, developing countries could make their own xanthan; its production is not affected by climate.

We discovered that xanthan added to doughs of either cassava or sorghum flour produced acceptable breads. The fundamental attraction of wheat to someone making bread
40 lies not in its taste but in the fact that the grain—unlike nearly all other cereals—contains substantial quantities of gluten. This protein has remarkable viscous and elastic properties. Wheat makes good bread because gluten enables dough to stretch and rise as it traps small bubbles of carbon
45 dioxide, produced by the yeast as it ferments. When the dough bakes, heat sets the glutinous dough round the bubbles, giving bread its characteristic spongy texture.

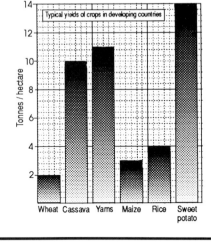

New Scientist

TASKS

a Describe how a *changeover to wheat can upset a country's economy* (line 4). (3)

b State *two* advantages of *bread bought in a market or shop* over local equivalent foods (line 14). (1)

c What *two* reasons are given in paragraph 3 for *not* growing wheat in tropical countries? (1)

d Using the information in the bar chart, construct a table to show the yield of crops in developing countries. (3)

e Describe how the properties of gluten in wheat make it an ideal dough for bread-making (lines 42–47). (2)

f Describe the role of yeast in breadmaking. (1)

g Name *two* ingredients which could be used in the making of a *new* bread and give the source of each (lines 31–38). (2)

14

When light shines on a cut shoot from the Canadian pond weed, Elodea, bubbles of gas are released from the cut end of the stem.
The rate at which bubbles of gas are produced can be used to measure the rate of photosynthesis.

An investigation was carried out to study the effect of different colours of light on the rate of photosynthesis in the Canadian pond weed.
1 The apparatus was set up as shown in the diagram

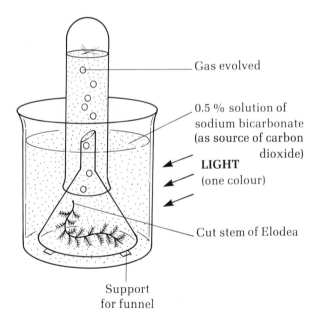

4 The procedure was repeated using a different colour of light of equal intensity
5 The results are shown in the bar chart.

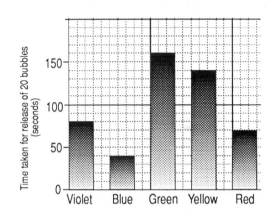

TASKS

a Which *two* colours of light are best for photosynthesis? (1)
b Without modifying the apparatus, how could the reliability of the results obtained at each colour of light be increased? Explain your answer. (1)
c Explain why the apparatus is left for 5 minutes at each colour of light before starting measurements. (1)
d Using the results obtained, find the average time taken for the release of 20 bubbles, for all the colours. (1)
e Express as a ratio the difference in the rates of bubble production under violet, blue and green light. (1)
f Using the results, explain how, when *white* light shines on a plant, the leaves appear to be green. (2)

2 The Elodea shoot was exposed to one colour of light and left for 5 minutes before measurements were taken
3 The time taken for the release of 20 bubbles from the cut end of the stem was recorded

Read the passage below and complete the tasks which follow.

WHERE DOES ALL THE GREEN GO?

The precise trigger and timing of autumn varies in different species and also depends greatly on the local climate. In Europe, the horse-chestnut (*Aesculus hippocastanum*) is among the first to turn yellow, as early as mid-September. Oaks (Quercus spp.) and alders (Alnus spp.) can remain green until November. A late spring or a drought in summer, can delay the onset of autumn by three weeks, while a warm wet spring and favourable conditions for growth in July can promote an early fall of leaves. Frost and persistent fog pockets in October can stimulate or delay the colour change in localised areas. The signal for the onset of chlorophyll destruction and ultimately, leaf fall, is thus apparently a combination of declining day-length and temperature, influenced by inherited factors and climate. The breakdown of chlorophyll in the autumn is part of a complex process. Plants salvage the useful sugars and nitrogen-rich compounds from the leaves during this process, transporting and storing them in seeds or underground tubers that will survive the winter. At the same time leaves break down their photosynthetic machinery. Chlorophyll and carotenoid (another pigment) are broken down to simpler parts, if not within the photosynthetic apparatus, then close by. In autumn leaves, the chlorophylls are usually degraded several days before the yellow carotenoids, so accounting for the golden hues of October. The flush of red colours that often accompanies the breakdown of chlorophyll appears to be caused by the conversion of numerous simple compounds to red or purple water-soluble compounds called anthocyanins. The graph shows the change in chlorophyll levels in the leaves of three different deciduous trees.

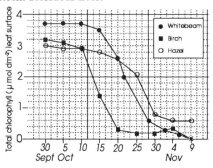

This first appeared in New Scientist

TASKS

a Using the results shown in the graph:
1. Which tree is last to start losing chlorophyll from its leaves? *(1)*
2. How many days does it take for the complete breakdown of chlorophyll in the birch leaf? *(1)*
3. Chlorophyll in the hazel leaf starts to breakdown on the 30th of September. Find the number of days it takes for 50% of the chlorophyll to be broken down. *(1)*

b Predict the effect on leaf fall of a warm, rain free summer. *(1)*

c What happens to the useful materials present in the chlorophyll, after it is broken down? *(2)*

d What explanation is given for the presence of the following colours in Autumn
1. yellow or golden colours
2. red colours? *(2)*

e Which *two* abiotic (environmental) factors are involved in the combination of factors which signal the onset of chlorophyll destruction? *(1)*

ANIMAL SURVIVAL

1 FOODTYPES

The pie charts below show the carbohydrate, fat and protein contents of five foods (A–E).

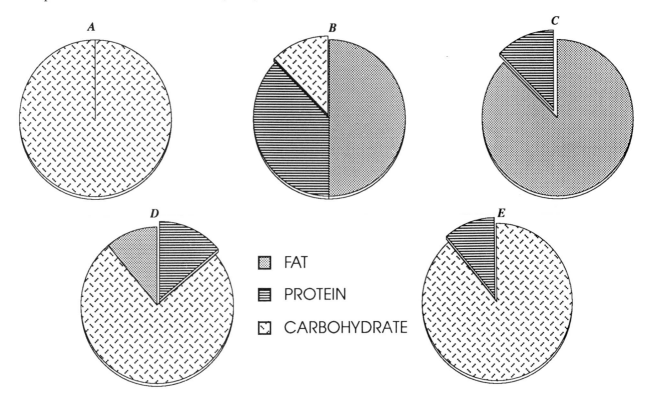

■ FAT

☰ PROTEIN

☑ CARBOHYDRATE

TASKS

a Which of the foods has
   1 only carbohydrate present
   2 no carbohydrate present?   (2)
b Protein is essential for growth in size.
   Which of the foods would be
   1 most beneficial for growth in size
   2 least beneficial for growth in size?   (2)

c A mass of fat gives twice the energy as an equal mass of protein or carbohydrate. Using this fact, identify which of the foods is the richest energy source.   (1)
d Calculate the mass of each foodtype in a 200 g sample of food B.   (2)

2 DIFFERENT DIETS

The bar charts opposite show the composition of the diets of two people.

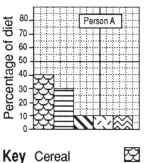
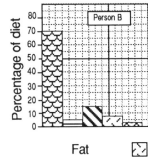

TASKS

a State the difference in the percentage of:
  1 cereal
  2 animal protein
  in the diets of the two people. *(2)*
b Which *two* components of their diets show greatest similarities? *(1)*
c What evidence supports the statement that person B is a vegetarian who might eat food such as milk and cheese? *(2)*
d Express as a ratio the difference in the percentages of cereal and fat in the diet of person A. *(1)*

3 TOOTH SENSITIVITY

The graph opposite shows the daily rhythm of changing tooth sensitivity, in volunteers whose teeth were subjected to the same pain stimulus.

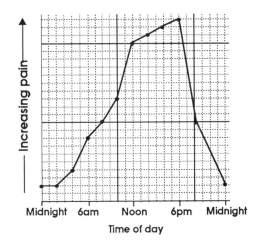

TASKS

a Using the graph, describe the daily rhythm of changing tooth sensitivity. *(2)*
b At what time of the day would a visit to the dentist be likely to be most painful? *(1)*
c Explain why dentists should treat their patients early in the morning. *(1)*

4 DAILY ENERGY I

The table shows the energy used by a typical teenager, doing different activities, during an average day. The number of hours spent at each activity are also shown.

Activity	Energy used (kilojoules/hour)	Time (hours)
Sleeping	240	8.5
Sitting	300	7.5
Standing	600	4.0
Walking	960	3.0
Running	3600	1.0

TASKS

a Calculate the total energy used by the teenager during an average day. (1)
b Express as a ratio the difference in the amount of energy used in sitting and in running. (1)
c How much more energy would the teenager use if instead of sleeping for 8.5 hours, he sleeps for only 8.0 hours and then runs for an extra half hour. (1)
d Construct a bar chart to show the energy used for different activities. (3)

5 DAILY ENERGY II

The graph shows the average daily energy requirements of males and females from 1 year to 20 years of age.

TASKS

a How many years does it take for the daily energy requirement to double in an average 3-year-old male and female? (2)
b At what age is the daily energy requirement at its greatest in the average male and female? (2)
c Over what age range is the daily energy requirement of males and females the same? (1)
d Given the fact that growth to full size is usually reached by the age of 20, explain why 20-year-olds have a lower energy requirement than 18-year-olds. (1)

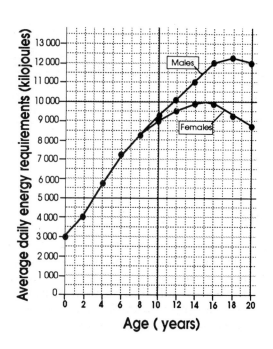

41

6 SENSITIVE TOOTHPASTE

Photograph 1 is a picture, magnified by a microscope, of part of the surface of a tooth which has become sensitive. Those things that look like craters are actually tiny channels, which lead straight down into the living nerve. So, when something that's cold (like an ice cream) or something hot (a cup of tea, perhaps) hits those channels, ..ouch!

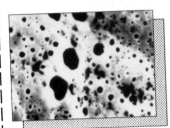

Photograph 1

Photograph 2

A Toothpaste which can actually shield the nerve. Simply brushing with Macleans Sensitive tooth paste is a quick way to help ease the pain. From the first day of use, it actually starts to fill in the channels so that the nerve becomes less sensitive. The filling builds up exactly where it is needed, and won't wash or brush off under normal conditions. The change in the surface of the tooth can be seen in photograph 2.

Macleans Sensitive toothpaste: all-round treatment for sensitive teeth.

The Macleans Sensitive active ingredients give you this protection quickly - in trial, after six weeks of regular brushing 83% of sufferers reported relief. Naturally, being Macleans we've also built in the fluoride that some other toothpastes for sensitive teeth lack, while ensuring that our formulation is especially low-abrasive, to protect the tooth from any further damage. Finally, if you ever thought that toothpastes for sensitive teeth had to taste salty, try ours. Macleans Sensitive has a fresh, minty taste that makes treating your sensitive teeth a pleasant experience.

MACLEANS SENSITIVE
ALL SENSITIVE TOOTHPASTES ARE NOT THE SAME

TASKS

a Account for the fact that when something cold *hits these channels ... ouch!* (2)

b How does this toothpaste help reduce tooth sensitivity? (1)

c If 83% of sufferers report relief, how many people, in a Macleans trial of 2000 sufferers, would report relief? (1)

d Why does the advertisement mention that the *formulation is especially low-abrasive*? (1)

e In such a trial there should be a control group. Which type of toothpaste should the control group be given? (1)

7 A CHRISTMAS DIGEST

In tests that measure how quickly food passed through the gut of volunteers, the remains of stained food first appeared in faeces at any time from 6.5 to 98 hours after feeding. In another classic experiment, subjects swallowed small coloured beads with their food. Although the majority reappeared within four days, some took a week or more over their journey. So traces of the roughage from a Christmas lunch may still be in motion—albeit slow motion—well into the New Year.

When waste arrives in the rectum, the signal goes out that defaecation is necessary. A nervous signal joins forces with conscious control to produce socially acceptable defaecation —in all but the most urgent cases. Faeces are about 70 per cent water. Of the remaining 30 per cent, bacteria from the gut make up a third; inorganic materials, such as calcium and phosphate, contribute one fifth and fat one thirtieth . Quantities of mucus, dead cells and a few proteins also add their weight to the proceedings. The rest is the famed dietary fibre. The remnants of a delicious Christmas meal have reached their proper end; no one mourns their passing.

This first appeared in New Scientist

TASKS

a On what basis did scientists develop methods for finding out *how quickly food passed through the gut of volunteers?* (2)

b What is the stimulus for defaecation? (1)

c Using the data above copy and complete the table to show the composition of faeces. (4)

Component	Percentage (%)
Water	70
Bacteria	
Inorganic matter	
Fat	
Mucus, dead cells, etc.	Negligible
Fibre	

d The table shows the average time that food remains within each region of the alimentary canal, where it undergoes digestion and absorption.

Illustrate this as a pie chart. (2)

Region	Time (hours)
Stomach	3
Small intestine	4
Caecum	1
Large intestine	16

Read the passage below and complete the tasks which follow.

WHAT HAPPENS IF WE HAVE BEEN DRINKING AT LUNCHTIME AND THEN DRINK AGAIN IN THE LATE AFTERNOON?

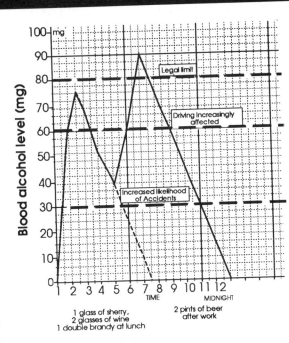

When alcohol is drunk, most of it is absorbed rapidly through the walls of the stomach into the bloodstream. The amount of alcohol in the blood rises gradually until it reaches a peak. The liver then has the task of destroying the alcohol. The graph shows the change in blood alcohol level of an adult male during a twelve hour period. He drinks during his lunch and then again after work.

TASKS

a After lunch, at 1 p.m., how long does it take for his blood alcohol level to peak? *(1)*

b What is the highest blood alcohol level during the time period shown? *(1)*

c How many hours does it take for his blood alcohol level to return to zero after peaking for the second time? Using this figure, calculate the rate of alcohol destruction per hour due to liver action. *(2)*

d For how many hours is he
  1 over the legal limit for driving
  2 at an increased risk of having an accident? *(2)*

9 OBESITY

The most important thing to do - if it's not too late - is to make sure you don't become overweight! As in most things, prevention is better than cure. In Britain, one in three people are seriously overweight.

5   1. Regularly check your weight against weight tables

2. Take lots of exercise

3. Make sure you *know* *which* *foods* are most fattening and cut down on these.

Often the most fattening foods are the least filling. Sugar, and
10 sugary foods and drinks give energy but no food value, and they don't really satisfy hunger. Try to eat less of these, and instead go for 'bulky ' foods like wholemeal bread, fresh fruit and vegetables and potatoes which, although filling, are - weight for weight - much less fattening than biscuits, cakes, crisps and
15 sweets etc.

4. Quite apart from its other health dangers, drinking too much can increase your weight rapidly. This isn't surprising, because alcohol has, weight for weight, *twice* the number of calories as sugar.

What is obesity?
20 Obesity means that your body is carrying more fat than it needs. When people use the word 'overweight' they really mean 'too fat'.

There are, of course, degrees of obesity. But, generally speaking, doctors consider a person obese if he's more than about 15%
25 heavier than the correct weight for his build.

But I'm already overweight!
In that case, there's nothing for it but to start a weight-reducing diet. If you really think you can't lose weight you should talk to your doctor. He will explain what to do. You will probably also need to step up your level of physical activity-perhaps join a local
30 keep fit class. Extra exercise - without overdoing things - will help speed up weight loss, and, therefore, encourage you to keep up your diet. Don't go for crash or fad diets. At best they are a

short term answer. At worst they can make you ill.

I'm not sure whether I'm obese
35 Here again your doctor will tell you if you really are unsure. The following method should give you a good idea of whether you're overweight:

40 (a) Lean forward slightly and pinch up a fold of skin over your stomach just below the rib cage
(b) If this is about an inch or more you definitely need to lose some weight.

What are the problems of being obese?
Besides the obvious problems of not looking and feeling as good
45 as you could, being constantly obese means you are more likely to get:
• High blood pressure   • Arthritis   • Bronchitis
• Gallstones   • Diabetes

The Flora Project

TASKS

a What percentage of people in Britain are classified as being overweight (lines 3–4)?   *(1)*

b Using the pictures, select *two* fattening foods which should be removed from the diet and select *two* foods which should be used to replace them (lines 9–15).   *(2)*

c What *three* pieces of advice are given to someone who is overweight and who wishes to lose weight (lines 5–8)?   *(2)*

d What is obesity (line 20)?   *(1)*

e Jane, whose height is 1.7 m, weighs 84 kg. The correct weight for her height and build is in the range 65–70 kg.
From the information in the paragraph *What is Obesity?*, calculate if Jane would be considered obese. Explain your answer.   *(2)*

f State with a reason whether or not the person shown in the 'pinch' test is overweight.   *(1)*

WHAT ADDITIVES ARE USED FOR

Taste

Flavourings. Since flavour is so important to our acceptance of food, it's perhaps not surprising to find flavourings are the most common type of additive.

Texture

Emulsifiers and stabilisers work together in many foods, doing the same sort of thing. An emulsifier will combine fats or oils with water; stabilisers prevent them separating out again.

Colour. There are 46 colouring additives allowed in food in Britain. Most are natural; some of these are extracted from plants. There are 17 artificial colours, E102 (a yellow colour) is one of the most common.

You'll find colours added to just about every type of processed food there is, except baby foods (for which there is a voluntary restraint).

Antioxidants. Fats and oils tend to go rancid sooner or later, usually because of a chemical reaction with air. Rancidity smells and tastes bad, and can be bad for you. So any food prepared with fats or oils - from biscuits to pork pies - is likely to contain an antioxidant.

Testing for additive safety. There's no standard test schedule for additive safety, although there are guidelines.

Most of the testing consists of feeding the additives to laboratory animals usually rats and mice - with different doses, over periods of up to two years. This should show up any toxic effects, including any birth defects. But tests of this sort have a number of limitations:

• tests on rodents cannot predict with certainty what the effects will be on man

• additives are almost always tested singly, whereas, in practice, they are rarely found singly. There is a possibility that they have different effects in combination.

What's in a Black Forest Gateau?
The ingredients in a chilled Black Forest Gateau are listed here under three headings (additives in bold type).
SPONGE
Wheat flour, Sugar, Liquid egg, Water, Fat reduced cocoa, Dried skimmed milk, Glucose syrup, Starch, Salt, **Flavouring, Colours** E102 E124 E122 E142 **Chocolate Brown HT, Emulsifiers** E475 E471
FILLING
Cream, Black cherries, Sugar, Glucose syrup, Modified starch, **Citric acid, Flavouring, Colours** E122 E142 E151, **Preservative** E211, **Stabilizers** E407
DECORATION
Cream, Chocolate flavour coating (sugar, vegetable fat, fat reduced cocoa powder, **Emulsifier** E322, **Flavouring**), Glace cherries (with **Colour** E127, **Preservatives** E202 E220, **Stabilizers** E407.

Which? magazine

TASKS

a Which type of additive is the most common and what reason is given for this? *(1)*

b Into which *two* groupings can colour additives be placed? *(1)*

c What reason can you give for the fact that manufacturers show a *voluntary restraint* by not adding artificial colour to baby food (Paragraph 4)? *(1)*

d What is the effect of oxygen on the storage life of fatty foods and how do food manufacturers lengthen the shelf-life of such foods (Paragraph 5)? *(2)*

e What *two* arguments are used by the author to show that conclusions drawn from testing additives on animals are questionable (Paragraph 6)? *(2)*

f Using the *Appendix*, identify *three* additives (from their 'E' number) which are used in the manufacture of Black Forest gateau. *(2)*

11 GOITRE

Attempts to eliminate goitre and cretinism in Nepal are being stepped up. Health workers have already injected two million Nepalis in the goitre-stricken areas of northern Nepal with an oil-based iodine preparation. The aim is to
5 prevent the severe iodine deficiency that leads to goitre. In Nepal, goitre affects half the population. In some of the more remote villages almost everyone displays the characteristic swollen neck of the disease.

Goitre and cretinism are caused by a deficiency of iodine.
10 The thyroid gland in the neck needs iodine to make a hormone called thyroxine. If people do not get enough io-

dine in food, the thyroid gland grows larger and
15 larger in an attempt to make up for the missing iodine.

Shortage of iodine
20 during pregnancy endangers the normal development of a foetus and can result in

25 babies being born with the severe physical and mental handicaps characteristic of cretinism. Some 4 per cent of Nepal's population are cretins.

The reason for the iodine deficiency in Nepal is largely geographical; years of soil erosion and flooding have
30 washed most of the iodine from the soil. And iodinated salt is not widely available.

The oil-based injection should provide the body with sufficient iodine for four years. It is intended only as a short-term solution, however. The long-term aim is to ensure
35 that everyone gets sufficient supplies of iodinated salt. But here, transport is the main problem.

Most of Nepal's salt is imported from neighbouring India. It often takes so long to reach people in the villages, or is stored for such long periods, that most of the iodine in the
40 salt evaporates before it is used. Nepal's Salt Trading Company is now setting up factories in the lowlands of the country which will add iodine to salt as it comes into the country.

In order to have any effect on Nepal's goitre problem the
45 company will have to be able to distribute the salt effectively, and in containers that will prevent evaporation of the iodine.

This first appeared in New Scientist

TASKS

a How is iodine used in the body? *(1)*

b What causes the *characteristic swollen neck* of goitre to develop (lines 7–8)? *(1)*

c Why is iodine deficiency so serious to the developing baby during pregnancy (lines 19–27)? *(1)*

d What *two* reasons are given for goitre being so common in Nepal (lines 28–31)? *(2)*

e What long term solution is given for curing the iodine deficiency? *(1)*

f Why, on reaching a village, does the imported salt *not* contain as much iodine as it should? How could this problem be overcome in the future? *(2)*

g Why is the injection of an oil-based iodine preparation only a short term solution (line 33)? *(1)*

h In certain areas of Britain, goitre used to be a common disease. What could you predict about the soil and water supply in such areas? *(1)*

12 BLOOD CHOLESTEROL

Read the passage below and complete the tasks which follow.

What is cholesterol?

Cholesterol is a 'fat-like' substance, which is produced in the bodies of all animals, including man. Although cholesterol is essential to our bodies, we produce enough for our own purposes and so, 5 strictly speaking, we don't need to eat any at all to stay healthy. However, as cholesterol is a normal animal product, all animal foods will contain some. Egg yolk is a very rich source, but organ meats (e.g. liver and kidney), shellfish (e.g. shrimps and 10 prawns), and dairy produce, such as cream and butter, also contain a lot of cholesterol.

Cholesterol and heart attacks

In Western countries many people have fatty deposits on the inside wall of their arteries. These deposits build up over a period of years and make 15 the channel of the artery narrower and narrower. This can interfere with the blood supply to the heart, and lead to a heart attack. A high level of cholesterol in the blood stream encourages the build up of these deposits, so increasing the risk of 20 a heart attack.

Is a high blood cholesterol level caused by eating too many cholesterol-rich foods?

Consistently high amounts of cholesterol in your food may increase the level of cholesterol in your blood stream. But blood cholesterol levels are affected much more by the changes in the 25 amount and type of fat we eat. (Remember that cholesterol is not strictly a 'fat'.) Foods which contain a lot of hard fat, otherwise known as 'saturated' fat, can raise the blood cholesterol level. However, soft or polyunsatu- 30 rated' fats can actually help to lower the amount of cholesterol in the blood. This is the reason why so many doctors and scientists agree that the kind of fat we eat is very important.

Here are some guidelines to help you! The following guidelines are those given by an important 35 British report on heart disease.

Cut down on these	Choose these instead
Fatty meat	Lean meat, chicken and fish
Butter	Margarines high in polyunsaturates
Fried foods	Grilled food
Lard and hard fats	Vegetable oil high in polyunsaturates
Cream, cakes and biscuits	Fresh fruit and vegetables

The Flora Project

TASKS

a Account for the fact that although cholesterol is essential for our health it is not required in our diet (line 3). (2)

b Why is it that most people have more cholesterol than they need? (1)

c Describe how high levels of cholesterol in the blood stream increase the risk of heart attacks (lines 12–20). (2)

d Of the factors which affect blood cholesterol levels, which factors are stated as having the greatest effect (lines 23–26)? (1)

e State the physical difference between saturated and polyunsaturated fats (lines 27–31). (1)

f Which foods are recommended to replace fatty meat and butter in the diet? (2)

g Other than avoiding fatty meat and butter, give two more recommended changes to your diet which could help to reduce your cholesterol intake. (2)

13 SUGAR SENSE

Read the passage below and complete the tasks which follow.

SUGAR - THE FACTS

There are two sources of added sugar: the sugar we buy in packets to add to tea and coffee, to sprinkle on cereal and to use in cooking - and the sugar that manufacturers add to processed foods and drinks.

5 Sugar is used not just for sweetness but also to get the consistency and texture the food manufacturers want - to make cakes light, biscuits crunchy, sauces smooth and so on. Sugar can also enhance flavours, and act as a pre-servative.

Too much sugar for our own good?

10 Sugar can lead to tooth decay. No-one disputes this fact; but there are differences of opinion about what else it does to us.

Fatness: all calories are the culprits

People who are overweight or obese run a greater risk than others of developing heart disease, high blood
15 pressure, diabetes, arthritis, and certain other diseases. No-one claims that sugar is the sole cause of being over-weight, even though sugary foods like cakes, sweets and biscuits are popularly thought of as 'fattening'. Sugar is no more 'fattening' than anything else.
20 But it is easy to eat sugary foods with other foods, thus boosting your calorie intake and making you more likely to put on weight.
Sugary foods are also easy to find room for even after a big meal.

Sugar and other diseases: a weak link

25 Some experts believe that a high sugar intake may be a factor in the development of other diseases. For some of these diseases, the link with sugar is via obesity. But eating a lot of sugary foods can also affect the balance in the rest of your diet. For example, you may
30 be getting too little fibre or too much fat. This lack of balance can in itself contribute to health problems!

Raisin and Ginger Cake
Ingredients: Wholemeal flour, Sugar, Invert sugar syrup, Raisins, Whole egg, Black treacle, Wheatflour, Animal
35 and Vegetable fats, Soya flour, Glucose syrup, Skimmed milk powder, Salt, **Emulsifier:** E471, **Flavouring, Colour:** Caramel, Extract of ginger, **Preservative:** E202.

TASKS

a What is the main theme of the passage? (1)

b What are the *two* sources of added sugar (lines 1–4)? (2)

c Select *three* ways in which manufacturers use sugar (lines 5–9). (2)

d Which harmful effect of sugar is now accepted by everyone? (1)

e Although *sugar is no more fattening than anything else* (lines 18–23) what reasons does the author give for sugar being the chief culprit for causing obesity? (2)

f Which *two* disorders of the circulatory system are related to obesity (lines 13–15)? (1)

g Other than the link with obesity, in what other ways is sugar linked to *health problems* (lines 25–31)? (1)

h In how many forms does sugar appear, in the ingredients list for the raisin and ginger cake? (1)

i Using the *Appendix*, identify the additives with 'E' numbers, used in making the raisin and ginger cake. (1)

Each nationality has its own language of posture and gesture, described as body language. But since body languages are often mutually incomprehensible, an innocent gesture made to a foreigner may well be an unwitting insult. There is no greater insult you can offer a Greek than to thrust your palms towards his face. This gesture, called the moutza, is descended from the old Byzantine custom of smearing filth from the gutter in the faces of condemned criminals as they were led in chains through the city. The meaning of a tug of the earlobe varies in the following countries:

to a Spaniard: *You rotten sponger*
to a Greek: *You'd better watch out mate*
to an Italian: *Get lost you pansy*

The meaning of the famous *A-OK* ring gesture varies in the following countries:
to an American: *Everything is all right*
to a Japanese: *Money*
to a Frenchman: *Zero*
to a Tunisian: *I'll kill you*

BAA plc

A Japanese passenger asks an American passenger if Heathrow Airport has a luggage trolley service. The American knows that the service is provided free and so gives the ring gesture. A Tunisian sitting beside a Greek businessman remarks, 'Did you see that!' and at the same time he pulls his earlobe due to being nervous. The Greek man loses his temper with the Tunisian and starts to shout at him. Meanwhile, a nearby waiter rushes forward and attempts to calm the situation, holding his two palms thrust out. The Greek promptly turns round and punches the waiter.

| TASKS |

a What is meant by body language? (1)
b Using the information on body-language, in the above paragraph, translate what each of the following has understood:
   1 The Japanese (1)
   2 The Tunisian (1)
   3 The Greek. (2)

15

The effect of altering the vitamin content in the diet of two similar groups of young rats is shown in the graph.

TASKS

a Removal of milk vitamins from the diet was after
20 days for the rats in Group A and
5 days for the rats in Group B.
Calculate the number of days which passed between the removal of milk vitamins and the start of a decrease in the average body mass for Groups A and B. *(1)*

b What evidence supports the statement that milk vitamins are stored in the rat's body? *(1)*

c Why are a group of rats used instead of an individual rat? *(1)*

d From the start of the experiment, how many days pass before the average body mass in each group doubles? *(1)*

e From the day on which the average body mass of each group starts to differ, how many days pass before the average body mass in each group is equal again? *(1)*

f Calculate the percentage decrease in average body mass of the rats in Group A from day 48 to day 58. *(1)*

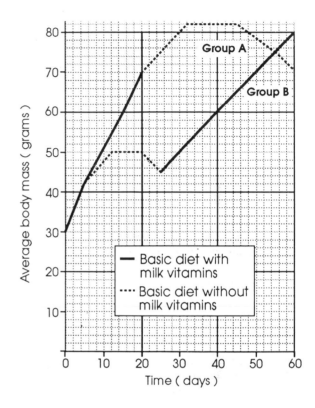

Chemically, bottled waters may be purer than some tap-water. But several brands did much worse than tap-water in bacteriological terms. Although none of the bottled waters we tested contained harmful bacteria, total numbers for some brands did exceed 10 000 bacteria per ml. The EC tap-water regulations don't allow levels as high as this but all the waters we tested came within EC requirements for mineral water. These say mineral water mustn't contain harmful bacteria, and set limits on total numbers of bacteria—but only for the first 12 hours after bottling.

On the whole, the sparkling waters contained much lower levels of bacteria. The difference in bacteria levels is probably partly due to the carbonation in sparkling water (to give it its 'fizz'), which makes the water slightly more acidic and thus less favourable to bacterial growth.

Overall, the bacteria levels of bottled waters we tested won't do you any harm, but the waters might not live up to your expectations of purity. And any water for a baby's feed should be boiled first.

KEY

Type of water—sparkling
A = carbonated natural mineral water: a still mineral water made sparkling by adding carbon dioxide

B = naturally carbonated natural mineral water: a naturally sparkling mineral water with carbon dioxide from the ground

Mineral content
Other than for bicarbonate and nitrates, 'high' levels of minerals at least exceed 'guide' levels in EC tap-water regulations: B = bicarbonate C = chloride F = fluoride M = magnesium N = nitrate P = potassium S = sulphate

Sodium content
Low = less than 20 mg per litre
Medium = between 20 and 150 mg per litre
High = more than 150 mg per litre (exceeds the maximum level in the tap-water regulations)

Sparkling	Type	Cost per litre (pence)	Mineral content Overall	Mineral content Type	Sodium
Badoit (France)	B	40	High	B.C.M.P.S.	High
Brecon Carreg (Wales)	A	30–40	Low		Low
Malvern (England)	A	30–40	Low		Low
Perrier (France)	B	50–60	Medium	N.S.	Low
Ramlosa (Sweden)	A	50–60	Medium		High
Safeway Braeuisge Spring (Scotland)	A	40–50	Low	F.	Low
Sainsbury's Scottish Spring (Scotland)	A	40–50	Low	C.	Medium
Spa Barisart (Belgium)	A	30–40	Very low		Low
Tesco Mountain Spring (Scotland)	A	0–50	Low		Low

Which? magazine

TASKS

a Which water is carbonated natural mineral water with a low overall mineral content and yet is high in fluoride? *(1)*

b State the *three* main differences between Perrier and Ramlösa mineral water. *(1)*

c Calculate the average cost of tap-water per litre, given that the average cost of bottled water is 30 p per litre and that this is 600 times dearer than tap-water. *(1)*

d Explain how these waters can be sold as mineral water and yet some of them do not meet with European Community tap-water regulations. *(2)*

e What reason is given for the low level of bacteria present in sparkling water compared with still water? *(1)*

f Explain why *any water* for a baby's feed should always be boiled. *(2)*

Read the passage and complete the tasks which follow.

New Scientist

Acidic mouth and how to fight it

The cause of decay is acid, which is produced by bacteria whenever someone rinses their mouth with glucose, or some other fermentable substance. A graph of acidity, expressed as pH, plotted against
5 time, shows how long it takes for the mouth to return to the resting (salivary) pH of about 6.7-6.8. This type of curve is known as a "Stephan curve". The rate at which pH returns to the resting value depends mainly on the amount and duration of
10 the glucose rinse, the rate of salivary flow, the buffering capacity of the saliva (that is, its ability to neutralise the acid).

If someone eats frequent sugary snacks, the pH of the mouth will probably not have returned to the
15 resting value before the next snack and subsequent bout of acid production. Constantly sucking sweets, for example, can keep a mouth acidic for prolonged periods. Acid removes minerals from tooth enamel, and saliva encourages remineralisa-
20 tion, creating a dynamic equilibrium. But at around pH 5.5, there is a net loss of mineral: a point described as the "critical pH". The longer that teeth are exposed to values around or below the critical pH, the more likely it is that they will start
25 to decay.

Drinking fluoridated water produces a low level of fluoride in the body. If this is present when teeth are forming, some fluoride is incorporated into the enamel of teeth, making it more resistant to attack
30 by acid. Fluoride toothpastes seem to act in another way, by promoting the remineralisation of early tooth caries.

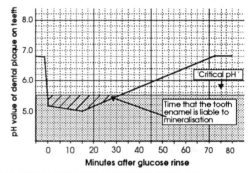

Minutes after glucose rinse

TASKS

a Explain how the acid which causes tooth decay is produced. *(1)*

b What does the Stephan curve show (line 7)? *(1)*

c From paragraphs 1 and 2, identify *two* important functions of saliva. *(1)*

d State the effect of acid on tooth enamel. *(1)*

e Explain what is meant by the term *critical pH* (line 22). *(1)*

f Explain why continuous sucking of sweets increases the rate of tooth decay. *(2)*

g Using the graph, answer the following:
  1 For how many minutes was the tooth enamel liable to mineralisation? *(1)*
  2 Which has the greater effect on mineralisation: a second glucose rinse 30 minutes or 40 minutes after the start? Explain your choice. *(1)*

h From the last paragraph, state the different effects on children's teeth of taking fluoride in the diet or using fluoride toothpaste. *(1)*

The diagram below represents a nephron from a human kidney. The arrows show the pathway followed by the fluid which filters from the blood into Bowman's capsule. The capillary network is responsible for the reabsorption of substances from the fluid as it passes along the length of the nephron.

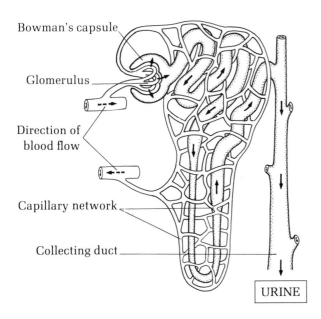

Bowman's capsule

Glomerulus

Direction of blood flow

Capillary network

Collecting duct

URINE

The table shows
1 the amount of each substance filtered daily from the blood into Bowman's capsule
2 the amount of each substance which is present in a day's output of urine.

Substance	1) Bowman's capsule	2) Urine
Water	180 l	1.5 l
Salts	1000 g	15.0 g
Glucose	200 g	0.0 g
Urea	40 g	40.0 g

a Calculate the percentage of filtered salts which are reabsorbed each day from the nephron. *(1)*
b Express as a ratio the differences in the salt, glucose and urea contents of the filtrate. *(1)*
c In terms of water content, by how much is the daily filtrate concentrated to produce one day's urine? *(1)*
d Calculate the concentrations (in grams/litre of water) of
  1 urea
  2 salt
  3 glucose
  in the filtrate and in the urine.
  Show the results as a table. *(4)*
e Explain why, despite being largely reabsorbed, salt has a higher concentration in the urine than in the filtrate. *(1)*
f Copy and complete the bar chart to show the amount of each substance filtered and the amount of each contained in the urine. *(2)*

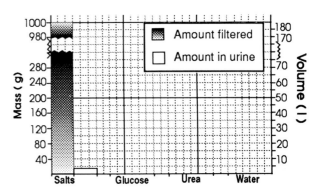

Read the passage below and complete the tasks which follow.

THE EMOTIONALLY RELATED TRANSPLANT

One of the great controversies in renal transplantation is whether it is ever right to take one kidney from a healthy person and transplant it into another person. The underlying biology on which this kind of transplant operation
5 relies is that although we are born with two kidneys, we can manage perfectly well with only one. Similarly, a person whose kidneys have failed does not need to have both kidneys transplanted. Therefore, an attractive proposition is to take one kidney from a healthy person
10 and transplant it into a person whose kidneys have failed. When renal transplants first began, the kidney was usually taken from a living close relative. This meant that little time was lost in transferring the kidney from one person to the other. Therefore, when it was connected to the recipient's blood circulation, it had sustained very little
15 damage. In contrast, a kidney removed from a dead person is usually stored for some hours before being transported and connected to the recipient's blood circulation. One other great advantage of using a living relative as a donor is that one can often expect less difficulty with the
20 problem of rejection.
In the early 1980's, the advent of a new anti-rejection agent, Cyclosporin-A, helped to solve this problem. This agent was so powerful that transplants from unrelated donors began to match the results from living related
25 donors. A graft survival rate per year of 80-85% was observed in transplantations where no relationship existed between the living donor and the recipient. This compared well with a survival rate of 85-90% seen in living related donor transplantations. The logical extension of
30 these results was to consider other possible living donors who did not have any genetic relationship to the recipient. The most obvious source was from husband to wife, or from wife to husband. This category became known as the "emotionally related transplant". It should be said, at
35 the outset, that not every spouse can be a donor to his or her "other half" because the donor must have a blood group which is compatible with the blood group of the recipient.

British Kidney Patients Association

TASKS

a What facts make it an attractive proposition to take a kidney from a healthy person and transplant it into a person whose kidneys have failed (lines 3–9)? *(1)*

b What are the *two* main advantages of using a kidney, from a very close relative, in a transplant (line 11)? *(2)*

c What reasons could be given for the fact that a kidney removed from a dead person may have sustained some damage? *(1)*

d How did Cyclosporin-A make it harder to argue that better results justified using *only* living related donors for transplants (line 22)? *(1)*

e Using Cyclosporin-A, what is the maximum difference in the percentage success rate for a recipient when receiving a kidney from a living related donor and an unrelated donor (lines 25–29)? *(1)*

f Explain what is meant by the term *emotionally related transplant* (line 34). *(2)*

g What reason could prevent a close relative such as a husband or a wife from being a donor? *(1)*

An investigation was carried out to study the response of woodlice to various humidities. Humidity was controlled in a series of choice chambers. The humidifying agent was altered to give a range of humidities expressed as a percentage of the maximum.

In a dry atmosphere woodlice lose water rapidly from their body surface.

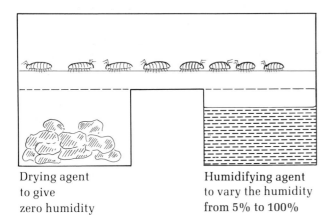

Drying agent
to give
zero humidity

Humidifying agent
to vary the humidity
from 5% to 100%

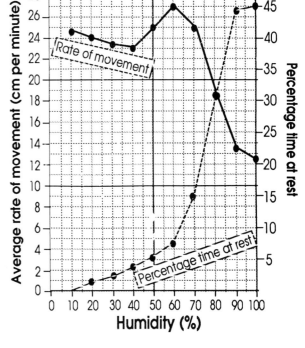

The graph shows the average rate of movement and average percentage time at rest for the woodlice at various humidities.

TASKS

a Explain why several woodlice are used in each trial rather than a single woodlouse. *(1)*

b Describe the behaviour of this species of woodlouse at a humidity of 20%. Explain the significance of this response for survival. *(2)*

c Identify the level of humidity at which the average rate of movement is 25 cm per minute and the average percentage time at rest is 5%. *(1)*

d Using the available data, calculate the distance covered by an average woodlouse in 10 minutes when the level of humidity is 70%. *(1)*

e Within what range of humidity does the most marked change in activity occur? *(1)*

4 INVESTIGATING CELLS

1 SINGLE CELLS

A teacher sets his pupils a task.
One pupil has to look down the microscope at a sample of stained tissue. He has to describe the structure of a single cell from the tissue. The other pupil has to make a drawing from the description given.

TASK

Draw a diagram to show the structure of this cell from the description given. *(3)*

Description
The cell is three times longer than it is broad. It has straight edges or sides which appear as narrow double lines. There is a thin strip of material lining the inner edge of the rigid outer structure. Embedded in this thin strip of material is a small, dark, oval structure. This structure is sited at the top, left corner within the thin strip. Also present within the thin strip are small, dark spots which give this area a dotted appearance. The centre of the cell appears to be empty of any structures and fills most of the cell.

2 CELL DIVISION

The graph shows the daily rhythm of cell division in human skin cells.

Energy is required for cell division and is produced by the chemical reactions of the body.

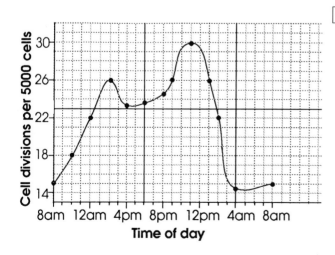

TASKS

a Describe the daily rhythm of cell division in human skin cells. *(2)*
b At what time do skin cells divide most rapidly? *(1)*
c At what times is the rate of cell division equal to 22 per 5000? *(2)*
d What is the increase in the rate of cell division per 5000 cells between 8 a.m. and 12 a.m.? *(1)*
e For how many hours does the rate of cell division remain above 26 per 5000? *(1)*
f Relate the shape of the graph, during the night, to cell activity. *(1)*

3 POTATO CUBES

The table below shows the effect of temperature on the mass of a potato cube placed in distilled water.

Temperature of water surrounding the potato	Percentage change in mass* (%)								
	Time (hours)								
	0	0.5	1.0	1.5	2.0	2.5	3.0	3.5	4.0
20 °C	0	+5	+7	+9	+12	+14	+16	+17	+17
50 °C	0	+7	0	−5	−8	−10	−10	−10	−10

*Note + represents a gain in mass
      − represents a loss in mass.

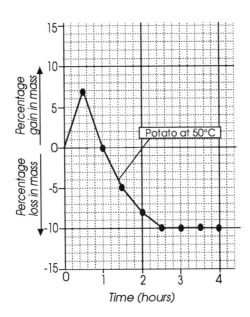

TASKS

a Copy and complete the graph for the percentage change in mass with time for the potato cube at 20 °C. *(1)*

b Given that the initial mass of both potato cubes used is 50 g, calculate their mass after 4 hours at the *two* different temperatures. *(2)*

c During which 1 hour period, at 20 °C, is there the greatest gain in mass? *(1)*

d During the first 30 minutes of both experiments what appears to be the effect of increasing temperature on the change in mass? *(1)*

e What evidence supports the statement that the cell membrane of a potato cell is destroyed at high temperatures? *(2)*

4 CELL SIZES

The unit used to measure the size of cells is the micron or micrometre (μm).

1000 microns = 1 millimetre

The drawing shows rhubarb epidermal cells as seen through a microscope. The diameter of the microscope field is 0.12 mm.

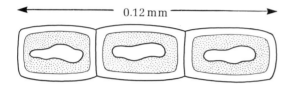

0.12 mm

TASKS

a Calculate the average length of a single rhubarb epidermal cell. *(1)*

b Given that a human cheek epithelial cell is, on average, only one quarter the length of a rhubarb epidermal cell, calculate the length of a cheek cell. *(1)*

c Given that a red blood cell is 7 micrometres (7 μm) in diameter, list the three different cell types in decreasing order of size. *(1)*

5 OSMOSIS

Osmosis is the overall flow of water from an area of high water concentration to an area of low water concentration across a selectively permeable membrane.

The following experiment was set up to investigate osmosis in living tissue.

TASKS

a 1 What changes have occurred in the experiment after 4 hours? *(1)*

  2 What conclusion can be drawn from the results? *(1)*

b What is the purpose of including the boiled potato in the investigation? *(1)*

c What acts as the selectively permeable membrane in the investigation? *(1)*

d Predict what would happen if a living potato was set up as in experiment A but with distilled water in the cavity and 10% sucrose solution in the beaker. *(1)*

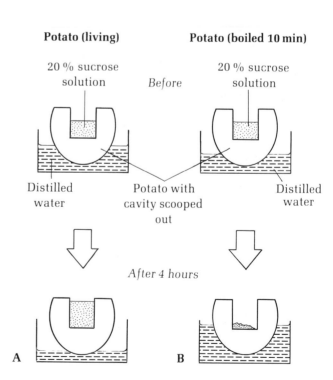

Potato (living)   Potato (boiled 10 min)

20 % sucrose solution   *Before*   20 % sucrose solution

Distilled water   Potato with cavity scooped out   Distilled water

After 4 hours

A   B

6 CATALASE

Catalase is an enzyme which is present in most living cells. To show that catalase is present in a tissue, the chemical hydrogen peroxide can be added. If catalase is present, bubbles of gas are given off.

An experiment was carried out to study catalase activity as shown in the diagram.

Experiment   *Control*

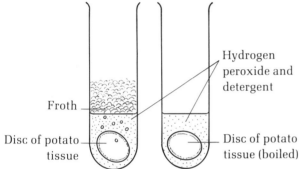

TASK

a Explain how the control experiment shows that living potato tissue contains the enzyme catalase.   *(2)*

Morag and Ross carried out an investigation to see which plant tissue contains most catalase.

Morag's Procedure

1 Using a cork borer, cylinders of tissue were cut from potato, celery, turnip and carrot
2 Discs, 2 mm thick, were cut from each cylinder of tissue
3 Two drops of detergent were added to each of four test-tubes (the detergent will froth when gas is given off in the catalase reaction)
4 Then 2 cm³ of a weak hydrogen peroxide solution was added to each of the test-tubes
5 A disc of each tissue type was added to a test-tube
6 The result was recorded as the maximum height to which the froth rose in each tube.

Results

Tissue	Height of froth (cm)
Potato	5
Celery	3
Turnip	3
Carrot	1

Ross's Procedure

1 Using a cork borer, cylinders of tissue were cut from potato, celery, turnip and carrot
2 Discs, 3 mm thick were cut from each cylinder of tissue
3 Four drops of detergent were added to each of four test-tubes
4 Then 2 cm³ of a strong hydrogen peroxide solution was added to each of the test-tubes
5 A disc of each tissue type was added to a test-tube
6 The result was recorded as the maximum height to which the froth rose.

Results

Tissue	Height of froth (cm)
Potato	12
Celery	8
Turnip	10
Carrot	5

Note: Diagram labels — Froth; Disc of potato tissue; Hydrogen peroxide and detergent; Disc of potato tissue (boiled)

b What similar conclusion can be drawn from both sets of results? *(1)*

c Select *three* stages in the procedures which could have led to the differences in the results. *(3)*

d Predict what would happen if a 2 mm disc of apple was added to a test-tube containing 2 drops of detergent and 2 cm³ of a weak hydrogen peroxide solution? *(1)*

e Using the results from Ross's experiment, construct a bar chart showing catalase activity in the different plant tissues. *(3)*

f What was the average height of froth obtained from the results of Morag's procedure? *(1)*

7 RESPIRATION

Read the passage below and complete the tasks which follow.

RESPIRATION

Living organisms and living tissues produce energy. A source of energy (substrate) and oxygen are required for energy release. The oxygen is required for the breakdown of
5 substrate molecules. As these substrate molecules are broken down energy is released. The organism uses this energy for functions such as movement and growth. However, some of the energy is lost as
10 heat. Carbon dioxide and water are formed during energy release. Energy release from a substrate occurs in a series of stages controlled by enzymes. Enzyme activity is affected by both temperature
15 and pH. Thus, when investigating energy release, both the temperature at which the investigation is carried out and the pH must be carefully controlled.

TASKS

a Using the appropriate letter, select from the list below, four observations which can be used to show that the energy release, described in the above passage, is taking place within living tissue. *(2)*

Letter	Observation
A	Decrease in oxygen concentration
B	Decrease in temperature
C	Production of carbon dioxide
D	Increase in mass
E	Decrease in mass
F	Increase in temperature.

b State *two* possible fates of the energy released within an organism? *(2)*

c Explain why experiments to investigate energy release are often carried out in a water-bath. *(2)*

d Respiration is the term used to describe energy release within living tissue. What *two* materials must be present for respiration to take place? *(1)*

e Suggest *one* reason why it is important that energy release *occurs in a series of stages* (lines 11–13). *(1)*

8 PAW-PAW

Read the passage below and complete the tasks which follow.

PAW-PAW

Enzymes have been of use to man for thousands of years. One example is the use of the enzyme papain by people living in areas of Africa. Much of the meat eaten in these areas
5 is very fibrous and tough. This type of meat would need to be cooked for hours to break down the fibrous protein, and so make the meat edible. The people in these areas have learned that after covering the meat with fruit
10 extracts from the paw-paw tree, for several hours, the meat is tenderised. The other important factor is that after cooking the process of tenderisation is stopped and the meat is no longer broken down. People not used to work-
15 ing with paw-paw fruit find that if they handle the ripe fruit with their bare hands, they can become very sore and reddened.

TASKS

a What is the main theme of the passage? (1)
b Suggest how papain brings about tenderisation of the meat. (1)
c What evidence supports the statement that high temperatures destroy enzymes? (1)
d Explain how ripe paw-paw has its effect on bare hands (lines 14–17). (2)
e Predict the effect of soaking meat in paw-paw extract for two days. (1)
f What commercial use could be made of papain in this country? (1)

9 ENZYMES AND pH

The graph shows the rate of reaction of two enzymes A and B, over a range of pH values.

TASKS

a State the pH range over which enzyme A is active. (1)
b At which pH is enzyme B most active? (1)
c State the pH range within which *both* enzymes are active. (1)
d At which pH value would the rate of reaction of enzyme A and B be equal? (1)

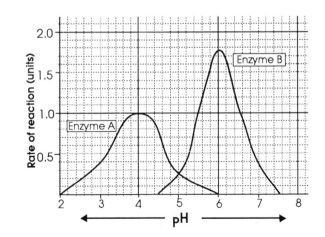

10 AMYLASE

An investigation was carried out to study the properties of the enzyme amylase, which breaks down starch to sugars. Five test-tubes were set up as shown in the diagram below.

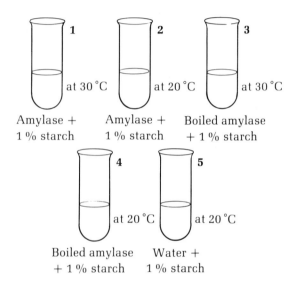

1 at 30 °C — Amylase + 1 % starch

2 at 20 °C — Amylase + 1 % starch

3 at 30 °C — Boiled amylase + 1 % starch

4 at 20 °C — Boiled amylase + 1 % starch

5 at 20 °C — Water + 1 % starch

The contents of each tube were shaken and immediately tested for starch, by adding 1 drop of iodine solution to 1 drop of the mixture in a small tube.

If starch is present a blue–black colour develops. The starch test was repeated after 10 and 20 minutes. The results are shown below.

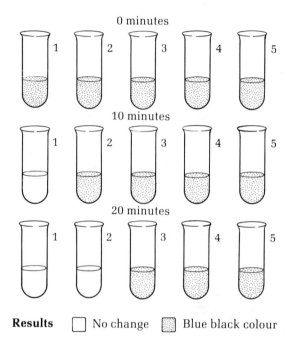

Results ☐ No change ▨ Blue black colour

TASKS

a Select *three* valid conclusions from the following list. *(3)*
  A Boiled amylase breaks down starch
  B The enzyme reaction occurs faster at 30 °C than at 20 °C
  C The enzyme is destroyed by heat
  D The results of tubes 4 and 5 are the same
  E Sugar is formed by the action of amylase on starch.

b To increase the validity of the results, *one* further experiment could be set up. Show the experimental set up by means of a labelled test-tube. *(1)*

c How could a more exact value of the time taken for the breakdown of starch be found? *(1)*

The following apparatus was set up to investigate the release of heat energy from respiring tissue. The investigation was carried out at a room temperature of 20 °C.

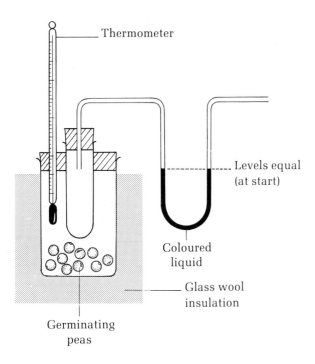

Germinating peas

Germinating peas were used as a source of respiring tissue. Temperature readings were taken every 2 hours. The results are shown in the table.

Time (hours)	Temperature (°C)
0	20.0
2	20.5
4	21.5
6	23.5
8	26.0
10	30.0

TASKS

a Copy the scales shown onto graph paper. Using the results in the table, construct a line graph of change of temperature with time. *(1)*

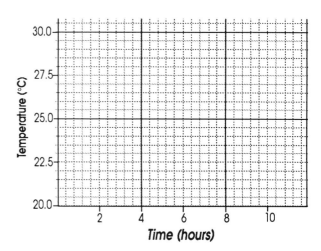

b What is the average increase in temperature per hour? *(1)*

c Describe the control experiment which should be set up in order to make the results valid. *(1)*

d Explain why the coloured liquid moves in the U-tube during the investigation. *(2)*

e What conclusion can be drawn from the results? *(1)*

f Predict the effect of each of the following changes:
   1 *no* glass wool insulation was placed around the container *(1)*
   2 the room temperature was at 18 °C? *(1)*

12 CANCER

Occasionally, cells in the human body change and become different from normal body cells. These unusual cancerous cells start to multiply in an uncontrolled way.

The table shows the percentage of men and women in the United Kingdom affected by common cancers.

Cancer type	Percentage of men	Percentage of women
Breast	0	22
Digestive organs	23	20
Respiratory tract	27	10
Skin	11	10
Reproductive and urinary system	18	13
Others	21	25

cigarettes cause lung cancer

Issued by H.M. Government

TASKS

a Copy and complete the bar chart showing the percentage of men and women affected by different cancer types. (2)

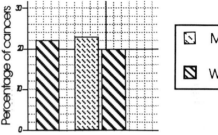
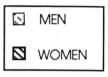

MEN

WOMEN

b Apart from breast cancer, which type of cancer shows a major difference in occurrence between men and women?
Explain how this difference may have come about. (2)

c If the number of women suffering from cancer of the digestive tract is 11 500, calculate the number of women suffering from breast cancer. (1)

13

Osmosis is the overall flow of water from an area of high water concentration to an area of low water concentration across a selectively permeable membrane. The greater the concentration of dissolved substances (solutes) the lower is the water concentration.

Examine the diagram below of a plant cell.

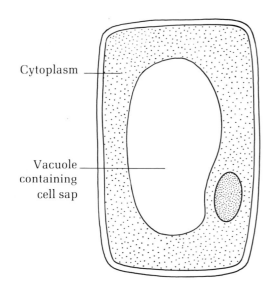

1 The cytoplasm acts as a selectively permeable membrane
2 The vacuole contains cell sap which contains substances dissolved in water
3 Water can flow by osmosis from the vacuole of one cell to the vacuole of an adjacent cell
4 The size of the vacuole will vary with the movement of water into and out of the cell.

The table shows the solute concentration, of the cell sap in the vacuoles of four cells, expressed in molar concentration (M).

Cell	Cell sap concentration
A	0.25 M
B	0.30 M
C	0.10 M
D	0.15 M

TASKS

Using the table, complete the following tasks.
a If the following cells are placed next to each other, state the direction in which there is an overall flow of water.
1 cells A and B
2 cells C and D
3 cells A and D
4 cells B and C. (2)
b In which of the cells will the vacuole appear to be largest? (1)
c Between which two cells, if placed together, is there the greatest flow of water by osmosis? (1)
d What would happen to the size of the vacuole in cell A when placed next to cell C? Explain your answer. (1)
e Which cell has the capacity to take in the greatest amount of water? (1)

66

A peptide molecule is a short chain of amino acids.

The following technique was used to find which amino acids were present in a peptide chain.
1 The peptide was digested by means of an enzyme
2 The digested mixture was spotted onto a square of filter paper at spot 1 as shown in the diagram
3 Different amino acids were also spotted onto the filter paper at spots 2 to 7 as shown by the table.

Number	Amino acid
2	Alanine
3	Glycine
4	Leucine
5	Methionine
6	Proline
7	Valine

4 The loaded filter paper was dipped into a suitable solvent

Before

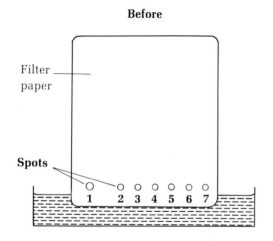

5 As the solvent rises up the paper the different amino acids are carried upwards at different rates
6 The results are shown on the filter paper marked **after**.

After

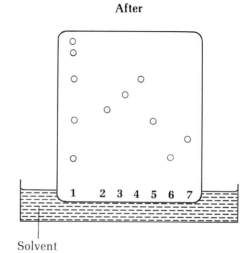

Solvent

TASKS

a Describe the role of the enzyme in this technique. (1)

b Why are the amino acids placed on the paper as well as the digested peptide? (1)

c How many types of amino acids are present in the peptide? (1)

d Name *three* of the amino acids from which the peptide is built. (1)

e Predict the effect on the results if a different solvent is used. (1)

Hannah and Alastair carried out an investigation to study the effect of temperature on the action of the enzyme pepsin, a protein-digesting enzyme.

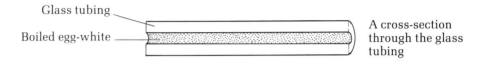

Glass tubing

Boiled egg-white

A cross-section through the glass tubing

This enzyme works best in acid conditions. The source of protein used, was egg-white which had been boiled inside narrow glass tubing. Hannah and Alastair worked in the same laboratory, where the temperature was 20 °C.

Alastair's procedure

1 Water baths were set up at 0 °C, 20 °C, 40 °C and 60 °C
2 A test-tube containing 10 cm³ of pepsin solution, 5 cm³ of 0.1 M acid solution and a glass tube containing boiled egg-white was placed in each of the water baths. The tube was cut to a length of 30 mm
3 The change in length of the egg-white in each tube was measured at 30 minute intervals over a three hour period.

The results are shown in the table.

Temperature (°C)	Reduction in length (mm)					
	Time (hours)					
	0.5	1.0	1.5	2.0	2.5	3.0
0	0.5	1.0	1.5	1.5	2.0	2.5
20	1.0	1.5	2.0	3.0	4.0	4.5
40	1.5	4.5	7.5	10.5	13.5	16.5
60	2.0	4.0	4.0	4.0	4.0	4.0

Hannah's procedure

1 Water baths were set up at 0 °C, 20 °C, 40 °C and 60 °C
2 Two test-tubes were placed in each water bath. One test-tube contained 10 cm³ of pepsin solution and the other contained 5 cm³ of 0.1 M acid and a glass tube containing egg-white. The tube was cut to a length of 20 mm
3 The test-tubes were left for 10 minutes after which time the pepsin solution was transferred to the other test-tube
4 The change in length of the egg-white in each tube was measured at 30 minute intervals over a three hour period.

The results are shown in the table.

Temperature (°C)	Reduction in length (mm)					
	Time (hours)					
	0.5	1.0	1.5	2.0	2.5	3.0
0	0.0	0.0	0.5	0.5	1.0	1.0
20	1.0	1.5	2.0	3.0	4.0	4.5
40	3.0	6.0	9.0	12.0	15.0	18.0
60	0.0	0.0	0.0	0.0	0.0	0.0

a Explain why at the start of Alastair's procedure, the contents of the test-tubes are not at the temperature they should be. (2)

b What evidence, from the results at 40 °C in both procedures, suggests that 30 minutes are required for the contents of the test-tube in Alastair's procedure to reach the desired temperature? (2)

c Using the results from Hannah's procedure, describe the relationship between temperature and enzyme activity. (1)

d Account for the difference in Hannah's and Alastair's results over the first 30 minutes at 0 °C. (2)

e Using Hannah's results at 40 °C, construct a line graph showing the effect of increasing temperature on enzyme activity. (3)

f Express as a ratio the difference between the breakdown of egg-white at 20 °C and 40 °C in Hannah's results after three hours. (1)

g What evidence from the results supports the statement that the room temperature in which Hannah and Alastair were working was 20 °C? (1)

16

The enzyme amylase causes the breakdown of starch to sugar.

An investigation was carried out to study the amount of sugar produced, in 15 minutes, over a range of temperatures from 0 °C to 30 °C. The results are shown in the table.

Temperature (°C)	Sugar yield (mg/15 min)
0	2
10	4
20	8
30	16

a State the relationship between an increase in temperature of 10 °C and the yield of sugar. (1)

b Predict the expected yield of sugar at 40 °C (this is the theoretical yield). (1)

c When the experiment was carried out:
1 at 40 °C, the actual yield obtained was greater than at 30 °C, but less than the theoretical yield
(The yield at 40 °C was 30 mg/15 min.)
2 at 50 °C, the actual yield was equal to that obtained at 30 °C
3 at 60 °C, the actual yield was zero.

Using the information above, plot a graph of yield against increase in temperature. (3)

d What evidence would support the following statements:
1 high temperatures do not cause the breakdown of starch to sugars
2 a temperature of 40 °C has a slight inhibitory effect on the action of the enzyme amylase. (2)

e Given that the theoretical yield obtained at 50 °C is 64 mg/min, using the result obtained in c, calculate the percentage difference between the theoretical yield and the actual yield. (1)

An investigation was carried out to find the concentration of the cell contents of potato tubers. The investigation was based on the fact that water will move into or out of the cells, depending on the concentration of the sugar solution surrounding the potato. If the concentration of the sugar solution is the same as that of the potato tuber cells then there will be no overall movement of water, and the mass of the potato will remain unchanged.

Yasmeen's procedure

1 Using a narrow cork-borer, seven cylinders of potato were cut out from a single potato
2 The cylinders were dried using filter paper, cut to a length of 4 cm and weighed
3 A cylinder of potato was placed in each of the following sugar solutions of known molarity (M): 0.10 M, 0.15 M, 0.20 M, 0.25 M, 0.30 M, 0.35 M and 0.40 M
4 The cylinders were left for 3 hours then dried and re-weighed.

Results

Sugar solution (M)	Mass of potato (g)	
	At the start	After 3 hours
0.10	50	65
0.15	50	60
0.20	50	55
0.25	50	50
0.30	50	45
0.35	50	40
0.40	50	35

Michael's procedure

1 Using a wide cork-borer, seven cylinders of potato were cut out from a number of potatoes
2 The cylinders were cut to a length of 4 cm and weighed
3 A cylinder of potato was placed in each of the following sugar solutions of known molarity (M): 0.10 M, 0.15 M, 0.20 M, 0.25 M, 0.30 M, 0.35 M and 0.40 M
4 The cylinders were left for 4 hours then re-weighed.

Results

Sugar solution (M)	Mass of potato (g)	
	At the start	After 4 hours
0.10	75	99
0.15	76	92
0.20	74	84
0.25	76	75
0.30	75	69
0.35	74	62
0.40	75	55

TASKS

a Whose procedure should give the more accurate results?
Select *one* aspect of the procedure which supports your choice. (1)
b Other than the aspect you have selected, give *two* other aspects of the procedures which do not allow for a fair comparison of results. (1)

c From Yasmeen's results:
  1 Which sugar solution has a concentration equal to the concentration of the cell contents? *(1)*
  2 Calculate the percentage gain in mass after 3 hours when the potato cylinder is placed in a 0.10 M sugar solution. *(1)*

d Given the fact that a 50 g cylinder of potato loses 20% of its mass when placed in a 0.35 M sugar solution for 3 hours, predict what the mass of an 80 g cylinder of potato would be after similar treatment. *(1)*

18

The cell membrane forms the living boundary of a cell and its function is to control the movement of materials into and out of the cell.

An investigation was carried out to study the chemical nature of a cell membrane, using the following procedure.
1 A cube of washed, fresh, beetroot was placed in a test-tube containing 10 cm³ of distilled water
2 An egg-white suspension was placed in a second test-tube. Egg-white contains protein which is denatured (its structure is altered) at high temperature
3 A thermometer was placed in each of the test-tubes
4 Both test-tubes were placed in an 80 °C water-bath and shaken continuously.

Results

After 4 minutes, when the temperature in both test-tubes was 60 °C:
 i the egg-white began to solidify
 ii the water surrounding the beetroot began to turn red, showing that red dye was passing out of the cells.

TASKS

a What conclusion can be drawn about the chemical nature of the cell membrane from these results. What evidence can be used to justify this conclusion? *(2)*
b Describe a control experiment which would show that it is high temperature and not the presence of distilled water which produces this effect on beetroot. *(1)*
c How could the experiment be improved to find the exact temperature at which the protein in egg denatures? Explain your answer. *(2)*

The uptake of oxygen by living organisms can be measured using the apparatus shown.

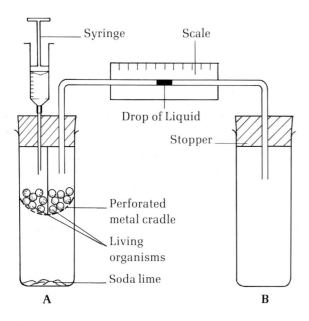

A   **B**

The experimental procedure is as follows:
1 The living organisms in tube A take in oxygen and release carbon dioxide
2 The carbon dioxide is absorbed by the soda lime
3 Absorption of the carbon dioxide causes a drop in pressure inside tube A. This is taken to be equal to the drop in pressure due to oxygen being used up
4 The drop in pressure is shown by movement of the drop of liquid towards tube A
5 Tube B acts as a control and should be identical in every way to tube A except for the presence of the living organism
6 The syringe can be used to return the drop of liquid to its original position

Two investigations were carried out on:
● 4 blow-fly larvae (maggots)
● 20 g of germinating peas.

The results are shown in the table.

Investigation	Distance moved by drop of liquid (mm)					
	Time (min)					
	0	10	20	30	40	50
Maggots	0	4.5	9.0	13.5	18.0	22.5
Germinating peas	0	8.0	16.0	24.0	32.0	40.0

TASKS

a Show, by means of a labelled diagram, how the control tube B should be set up. (2)
b What conclusion can be drawn from both of the investigations? (1)
c Using the data, construct a line graph to show the distance moved by the drop of liquid with time, for both investigations. (4)
d Explain, with a reason, whether or not you think the following conclusion is valid.
The rate of oxygen uptake by germinating peas is greater than that of maggots. (1)
e Predict the distance moved by the drop of liquid, after 1 hour, in the investigation on the maggots. (1)
f Predict the results obtained if 30 g of peas are used in an identical investigation. (1)
g How could the syringe be used to obtain a measurement of the volume of oxygen used up in 1 hour. (2)

5 THE BODY IN ACTION

1 OSTEOPOROSIS

Read the passage below and complete the tasks which follow.

False claims in milk ads, say doctors

Doctors have attacked as misleading a national advertising campaign to sell milk to people who are anxious about the crippling bone disease, osteoporosis.

5 The campaign is based on the dairy industry's belief that extra calcium can prevent osteoporosis, a thinning of the bones that leaves one in four older women and one in 40 men vulnerable to sudden fractures. The most
10 common underlying cause is hormonal change during menopause.

Yet almost all doctors accept that for adults, extra calcium is much less important than hormone supplements, the only known effective
15 treatment for the disease. These can delay the onset of fractures by about 10 years — if prescribed early enough.

Two years ago a panel of experts from Europe, the United States and Australia concluded that,
20 although a high calcium intake was important to build bones in childhood and adolescence, only oestrogen could treat the disease in older people. Calcium is often given as well but there is no evidence that it works on its own.

25 The poster is part of a £10m drive by the National Dairy Council paid for by farmers and the dairy industry to reverse the slump in milk sales caused by publicity linking heart disease with saturated fats.

Worried about osteoporosis?

Consult a specialist

Ask your milkman for more information about calcium

Sunday Times 30th April 1989

TASKS

a What is osteoporosis and state the danger associated with this disorder (lines 7–11)? (2)

b Why do doctors say that the claims made in milk advertisements are false (lines 23–24)? (1)

c What is the medical treatment for osteoporosis and when is it recommended that treatment should begin (lines 12–17)? (2)

d What *two* conclusions do the panel of experts come to, about calcium intake in the diet (lines 18–23)? (2)

e From the passage name *one* other compound present in milk, and the health disorder with which it is associated. (2)

f Express as a ratio the difference in the number of women and men suffering from osteoporosis (lines 5–9). (1)

2   SPORTS INJURY

A common sporting injury to affect the knee is chondromalacia patellae. This is a disorder of the muscle component which helps to hold the patella (knee-cap) in its proper position when the leg is held straight. This causes either a loss in the strength of muscle contraction or a loss in muscle bulk. Pain is usually felt after or during exercise, when sitting for long periods of time with the knee bent, or when going up or down stairs.

The table shows the percentage of cases of chondromalacia patellae arising from different sports.

Sport groups	Percentage (%)
Football	25
Rugby	7
Hockey	3
Judo/gymnastics	7
Running	20
Netball	5
Racket Games	14
Skiing	5
Cycling	5
Rowing	9

TASKS

a Which *three* sports account for more than 55 % of people suffering from chondromalacia patellae? *(1)*

b Even though 25 % of sufferers play football, why is it inaccurate to say that playing football increases the chance of suffering from the condition more than playing other sports? *(1)*

c Explain why exercising the muscle component, when the leg is straight, helps to relieve the condition. *(2)*

3   WALKING AND BREATHING

The graph opposite shows the volume of air breathed in and the number of breaths taken per minute, when walking at different speeds.

TASKS

a Calculate the volume of each breath when walking at 9 km/hr. *(1)*

b Calculate the percentage decrease in the volume of air breathed per minute when slowing from 9 km/hr to 2 km/hr. *(1)*

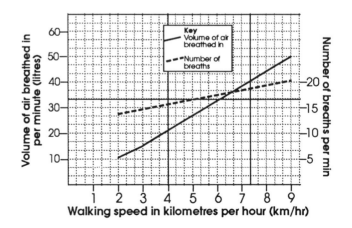

c Using the graph, predict what the number of breaths per minute would be when walking at 1 km/hr. *(1)*

d What advantage would there be in taking many measurements from one person at each walking speed? *(1)*

e Describe the changes which occur in breathing during increased exercise. *(2)*

4   CIRCULATION

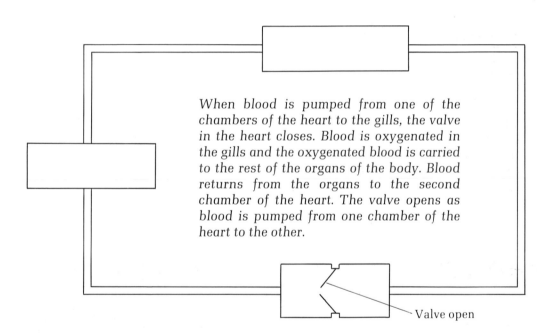

When blood is pumped from one of the chambers of the heart to the gills, the valve in the heart closes. Blood is oxygenated in the gills and the oxygenated blood is carried to the rest of the organs of the body. Blood returns from the organs to the second chamber of the heart. The valve opens as blood is pumped from one chamber of the heart to the other.

Valve open

TASKS

Copy the diagram above which shows the outline of the circulatory system of a fish. Using the information in the passage, complete the boxes and indicate, using arrows, the direction of the blood flow. *(2)*

Read the passage below and complete the tasks which follow.

Glasgow Herald

Taking coronary warnings to heart

First the good news. Fewer Scotsmen are dying from coronary heart disease. Mortality figures show that among the under-45's the improvement verges on the dramatic. Now the bad news. First, in the older age group, where coronary heart disease is far more common, the death rate has barely changed. In 1976 it claimed 1650 in every 100 000 men in the 65 to 69 age group compared with 1500 in 1986. The news for Scots women is even grimmer. Though fewer women than men die from heart disease, the figures are still the worst in the world. The three risk factors associated with heart disease are smoking, high levels of blood cholesterol and high blood pressure. There is a growing conviction that the real villain of the three is cholesterol. Too much cholesterol can lead to a narrowing of the arteries, increasing the risk of a heart attack. Supporters of the cholesterol theory point to the United States where doctors and educators have waged war on cholesterol for two decades and where there has been a dramatic drop in heart deaths. They also point to Japan where nearly all the men smoke like chimneys and hardly any of them have heart attacks. The Japanese diet happens to be extremely low in cholesterol. Professor Hugh Tunstall Pedoe of Dundee believes that it is the combination of high cholesterol and smoking which puts the Scot at particular risk. And though he believes the anti-smoking message may be getting through to some sectors of the population, he reckons most of those in the risk groups haven't done enough to change their diet. So what are the hopes of a long-term decline in mortal-

ity from coronary heart disease in Scotland? There are some grounds for optimism. Dr Lindsay Davidson runs the Good Hearted Glasgow Campaign, Greater Glasgow Health Board's attempt to chivvy unhealthy Glaswegians into a healthier lifestyle. An initial pilot study showed that citizens are pretty well aware of the risks associated with smoking, poor diet and lack of exercise but reluctant to do anything about their own lifestyles. "The problem is not lack of information, but lack of motivation," says Davidson.

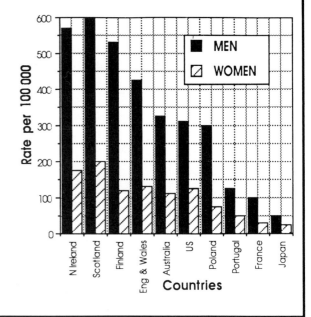

TASKS

a What is the good news for Scotland and what are the *two* pieces of bad news (lines 1–4)? *(3)*

b Which of the three risk factors, when in excess, is thought to be the real villain? Describe its effect (lines 13–15). *(2)*

c How do the results from the United States add support to the cholesterol theory (lines 16−20)? *(1)*

d Why does a low rate of heart attack and yet a high level of smoking among the Japanese *not* conflict with Professor Pedoe's belief of why the Scot's are at high risk (lines 20−26)? *(2)*

e In which *three* ways would Dr Davidson motivate the citizens of Glasgow to reduce their mortality rate due to coronary heart disease (lines 36−41)? *(2)*

f From the bar chart, express as a ratio the difference in the coronary heart disease mortality rate for men and women in Scotland. *(1)*

6 BLOOD GLUCOSE AND INSULIN

The graph below shows the average variation in the levels of blood glucose and insulin over a 6 hour period, for ten people with normal glucose levels. (A normal blood glucose level is 100 mg per 1 cm³.)

Two meals and a period of exercise were taken at the times shown.

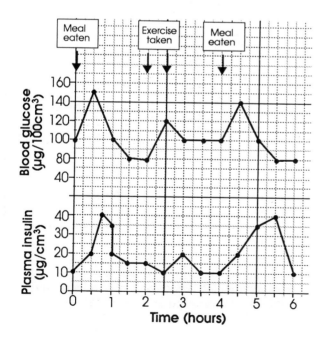

TASKS

a What effect, on the blood glucose and insulin levels, do the following have:
  1 a meal
  2 a period of exercise? *(2)*

b What evidence supports the statement that insulin causes a decrease in blood glucose level? *(1)*

c Why is it good experimental procedure to:
  1 take the average level for a *group* of people rather than for a single person
  2 use only people with normal glucose levels? *(2)*

d How long after a meal does it take for the blood glucose level to return to normal? *(1)*

7 BLOOD VOLUME

The table shows the volume of blood pumped per minute to muscles and the rest of the body, in three different people.

Subject	Volume of blood (litres/minute)	
	to muscles	to rest of body
Average man at rest	6.0	5.5
Average man exercising	20.0	5.0
Male athlete exercising	30.0	5.0

TASKS

a Construct a bar chart to show the blood flow in each person. (3)

b Express as a ratio, the difference in blood flow to the muscles in the man at rest and the exercising athlete. (1)

c If the average man and the male athlete were to exercise, at the level shown, for 15 minutes, calculate the difference in blood volume reaching their muscles during that time. (1)

8 PULSE

A pulse is the expansion of an artery caused by blood passing through after a contraction of the ventricle in the heart.

When a person is at rest the left ventricle pumps out 70 cm³ of blood every time it contracts.

To calculate the blood output per minute from the left ventricle, the number of pulses per minute is multiplied by the blood volume pumped out (70 cm³).

Karen and Andrew use this information to compare the output per minute of their own left ventricles when at rest.

Karen's procedure, she

1 sits on a stool at a bench for ten minutes
2 counts her pulse for 30 seconds and doubles her answer
3 repeats stage 2 twice, calculates the average and gets 70, 72 and 68 beats per minute
4 multiplies the average by 70.

Andrew's procedure, he

1 lies down on a bench for two minutes
2 counts his pulse rate for 30 seconds, doubles his answer and gets 78 beats per minute
3 multiplies this answer by 70.

TASKS

a 1 Select *two* aspects of the experimental procedures which do *not* allow a fair comparison of the results. (2)

  2 Describe how you could eliminate these two sources of error. (1)

b Using the results, calculate the difference between the volume of blood pumped out from the left ventricles of Andrew and Karen, in one minute, when at rest. (1)

Government
Information 1987

WHAT IS HIV INFECTION?

AIDS (Acquired Immune Deficiency Syndrome) is just one of four possible outcomes of infection by the Human Immunodeficiency Virus (HIV). This virus attacks the body's immune system by destroying cells which are vital in the protection of the organism against infection. The virus is not directly responsible for the infected person's subsequent illness. Rather, by destroying the person's immune system, it enables other infections to take hold. These other infections are usually described as 'opportunistic infections', because, in the absence of the opportunity afforded by HIV infection, they are normally harmless.

HOW IS HIV TRANSMITTED?

The virus has been isolated in: blood, blood-products (such as plasma), semen, vaginal secretions, tears, saliva and urine. The identification of the virus in body fluids such as tears, saliva and urine has led to concern about the risk of transmission of infection through kissing, spitting, sharing crockery and cutlery. It is important to emphasise that although the virus has been isolated from these body fluids and it has been possible to grow or culture it under sophisticated laboratory conditions, there is no documented evidence that the infection is transmitted in these ways. This particular virus is extremely fragile - it cannot survive, for example, in a swimming pool, in an ordinarily hot washing-up bowl, or on a toilet seat. The transmission of HIV depends not solely upon substances but also upon activities. There are three ways in which the infection might be spread:

1. Sexual Transmission
2. Transmission of blood
- Injecting drugs
- Donation of infected blood, blood products, organs, grafts, (becoming increasingly rare in United Kingdom because of intensive screening processes and heat treatment of blood products)
- Exposure of skin wounds to large amounts of infected blood and body fluid
3. Transmission from mother to baby
Mother-infant infection which may happen either crossplacental, during the birth process, or through breast feeding.

TASKS

a What is the main theme of the passage? *(1)*

b How does the HIV virus attack the body (Paragraph 1)? *(1)*

c Explain why the HIV virus is not directly responsible for an infected person's illness (Paragraph 1). *(2)*

d Why has *identification of the virus in body fluids such as tears, saliva and urine* given cause for concern (Paragraph 2)? *(1)*

e What information in paragraph 2 helps to reduce the cause for concern? *(1)*

f What information suggests that the HIV virus cannot survive for long, outside of the human body (Paragraph 2)? *(1)*

g Transmission of the HIV virus *depends not solely upon substances but also upon activities* (Paragraph 2).
Copy and complete the table using information in the last section. *(3)*

Activities	Substance exchanged
	Semen and vaginal fluids
Needle sharing by drug users	
	Human milk

h Why, in the United Kingdom, is the HIV virus no longer spread through blood transfusions? *(2)*

10   BLOOD FLOW

The bar chart opposite shows the rate of blood flow to different organs and tissues when the body is at rest.

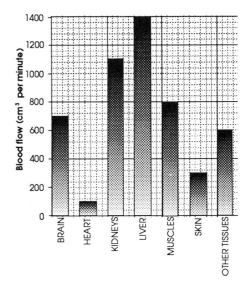

TASKS

a What is the **total** volume of blood flow per minute to all the organs and tissues? *(1)*

b What percentage of the total blood flow per minute goes to the kidneys? *(1)*

c Express as a ratio the difference in the blood flow to the muscles, skin and heart. *(1)*

d How long does it take for 7 litres of blood to pass through the brain? *(1)*

11   SQUEEZING MUSCLES

Kevin and Rita carried out an investigation to find if muscles get tired with repeated use. They set up the following experiments.

Rita's procedure

1 Using her right hand she squeezed a hand grip until it registered a force of 50 newtons
2 She relaxed her grip and rested for 5 seconds
3 She repeated stages **1** and **2** until she could no longer exert a force of 50 newtons.

Results: After 50 attempts Rita could no longer produce a reading of 50 newtons.

Kevin's procedure

1 Using his left hand he squeezed the hand grip as hard as he could
2 He relaxed his grip and then, squeezed again as hard as he could
3 This was repeated until he could no longer manage to squeeze the hand grip.

Results: After 42 attempts Kevin could no longer manage to squeeze the hand grip.

TASKS

a Select *two* aspects of the procedures which do not allow a fair comparison of the results. Give a reason for selecting each. *(4)*

b What justifiable conclusion can be drawn from the results of both experiments? *(1)*

c Predict what the effect on the results of Rita's experiment would be if she repeated her procedure but relaxed for 10 seconds between each squeeze of the hand grip. *(1)*

12 WEIGHT TRAINING

The table below shows the effect of weight-training on the strength of three people. The initial maximum lift for each person was 100 kg. This value was taken as the initial strength.

Each person was trained using a different percentage of the maximum lift.
(Training with 25 % of the maximum lift means training with a 25 kg mass.)

Percentage of maximum lift used in training	Change in strength with training (kg) (shown as maximum lift)		
	After 10 weeks	After 20 weeks	After 30 weeks
25 %	100	100	100
50 %	125	125	125
75 %	150	175	190

TASKS

a State the relationship between the mass used in training and the change in strength. *(1)*

b Copy the graph and plot the missing curve for the change in strength of a person, when trained at 75 % maximum lift. *(1)*

c If a person is training at 75 % maximum lift, calculate:

    1 the percentage increase in strength after 30 weeks *(1)*

    2 the average weekly % increase in strength after 30 weeks. *(1)*

d Predict the effect of 20 weeks training with a 75 % lift (75 kg mass) followed by ten weeks training with 100 % maximum lift. *(1)*

e During which period of training does the greatest gain in strength occur? *(1)*

f Select *one* factor which would be kept constant, to allow a fair comparison of the results of the three people. *(1)*

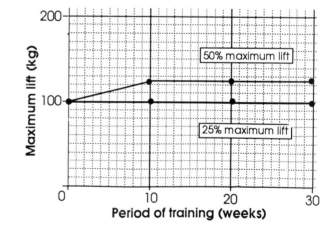

13 STEROIDS

Metabolism is the sum of all chemical processes which occur in the living cells of an organism. Anabolic steroids are man-made chemicals which have a variety of effects on metabolism. In females, anabolic steroids
5 regulate the protein in connective tissue and bone. They inhibit the pituitary gland's ability to produce the hormones which stimulate the ovaries into producing their hormones. They affect the development of internal and external female organs. If a woman, pregnant
10 with a female child, takes anabolic steroids, these drugs will have a "masculinising" effect on her unborn baby. Even in adult women, these undesirable masculinising effects can be irreversible. Many Soviet and East German women who took anabolic steroids and
15 developed low voices and beards are now stuck with them. These steroids also allowed them to train more, and so put on more muscle. In both men and women, anabolic steroids can break down genetic patterns in the nucleus of the body's cells; affect the absorption of
20 calcium into the bones; stop bone growth in young people who have not yet reached their full height; and destroy the liver whose function it is to destroy alien synthetic chemicals such as anabolic steroids. Because of the potential damaging effects of anabolic steroids
25 on the genetic material in the nucleus of the cell, many women athletes who have taken anabolic steroids, are now afraid to have children. Says Renate Vogel Heinrich, who nine years ago was a champion East German swimmer and who was brought up on anabolic ster-
30 oids: "I would love to have children, but I am afraid that I would bring them into the world handicapped."

YOU THINK WE'VE PUSHED THIS STEROID THING TOO FAR!

JUNIOR CHAMP

TASKS

a What is the main theme of the passage? *(1)*

b Copy and complete the table to show the effects of anabolic steroids and the organs affected. *(3)*

Organ affected	Effect of anabolic steroid
	Inhibit hormone production
Ovaries	
	Reduce absorption of calcium
Liver	

c What are the *two masculinising effects* of anabolic steroids on an adult female (lines 13–16)? *(2)*

d Why would young people taking anabolic steroids fail to attain their full height? *(1)*

e Which *two* of the effects of anabolic steroids would support the attitude of Renate Vogel Heinrich towards having children (lines 9, 12, 23–27)? *(2)*

14

The composition of blood changes as it passes through the lungs. 100 cm³ of blood entering the lungs has 0.9 cm³ of nitrogen, 10.6 cm³ of oxygen and 58.0 cm³ of carbon dioxide. Blood leaving the lungs has 0.9 cm³ of nitrogen, 19.0 cm³ of oxygen and 50.0 cm³ of carbon dioxide.

TASKS

a Use the data to construct a table of blood gas volumes passing through the lungs. *(2)*
b Calculate the percentage change in volume, as the blood passes through the lungs, of:
  1 oxygen
  2 carbon dioxide. *(2)*

15

Genetic (inherited) factors influence many aspects of fitness and physical performance. Studies show that lung size and efficiency of gas exchange are influenced by genetic factors.

Training can increase the maximum oxygen uptake by a factor of 35 % for an untrained individual. The increase, however, is limited to 35 % due to the limitations imposed by the individual's genetic factors.

Good oxygen uptake in the lungs ensures that the muscles receive sufficient oxygen for energy production.

The table below shows the maximum oxygen uptake for three people when untrained and after a period of training. It also shows the difference in uptake between the trained and and untrained stages.

TASKS

a Construct a bar chart to show the maximum oxygen uptake for each person *before* and *after* training. *(4)*
b Name the genetic factors which could influence maximum oxygen uptake. *(1)*
c Account for the fact that a person who is already partly trained cannot achieve a 35 % increase in their maximum oxygen uptake. *(2)*
d To become a top class 400 m runner requires a maximum oxygen uptake of 81 cm³/min/kg. What is the *minimum* value for maximum oxygen uptake an untrained person would need to have, if they are to be trained to become a top class 400 m runner. *(2)*

Person	Maximum oxygen uptake (cm³/min/kg)		Difference
	Before training	**After training**	
A	30.0	40.0	10.0
B	40.0	54.0	14.0
C	50.0	67.0	17.0

The graph below shows the volume of air in each breath, for a man both at rest and during strenuous exercise.

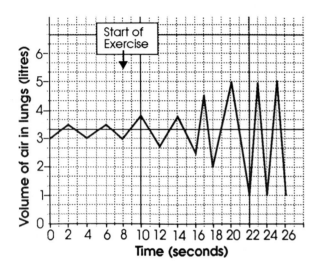

a Express as a ratio the difference in the rate of breathing when at rest and the settled rate during strenuous exercise. *(1)*

b By how many times does the volume of a breath increase when changing from rest to strenuous exercise? *(1)*

c Calculate the rate of breathing per minute during strenuous exercise. *(1)*

d Using the data, describe *two* effects of exercise on breathing. *(1)*

The table shows the average number of red blood cells in the blood of people living at different altitudes.

Each reading is the average for ten male adults, who have lived at that altitude for at least four months.

Altitude (metres)	Average number of red blood cells (millions/mm³ of blood)
Sea level — 0	5.1
1500	5.3
3000	5.4
4500	5.6
6000	5.9
7500	6.2

TASKS

a Draw a line graph to show the change in the average number of red blood cells with increasing altitude. *(3)*

b Calculate the average increase in red blood cells with each 1500 m increase in altitude. *(1)*

c Explain why at each altitude:
  1 the average of ten adults was taken
  2 the people have lived at that place for
  at least four months. *(2)*
d The amount of oxygen present in the air
  decreases with increasing altitude. Red
  blood cells contain the pigment haemoglobin which combines with oxygen in
  the lungs and carries it to the tissues.

Using this information, account for:
  1 the results in the table *(2)*
  2 the fact that many top athletes include
  several months of training at high altitude as part of their preparation for a
  major event. *(2)*

18

The following methods may be used to calculate
the blood volume of an adult male.

Method 1

1 2000 units of a dye are injected into a vein
2 The blood is allowed to circulate for 5 minutes
3 15 cm³ of blood is withdrawn with a syringe
4 The amount of dye present is analysed.

Result: 5 units of dye are present in the sample.

Calculation

$$\frac{\text{Amount of dye injected}}{\text{Volume of blood}} = \frac{\text{Amount of dye in sample}}{\text{Volume of sample}}$$

Method 2

This method involves the use of a radioactive
isotope of iodine. Radioactive isotopes are un-
stable and breakdown at a characteristic rate.
The breakdown or disintegration can be detected
using a Geiger counter.

1 1 cm³ of the radioactive isotope of iodine is
  injected into a vein. The rate of disintegration
  of the isotope gives a reading of 600 000 counts
  per minute

2 The blood is allowed to circulate for 5 minutes
3 1 cm³ of blood is withdrawn
4 The rate of iodine disintegration in the sample
  is measured.

Result: The rate of disintegration is 100 counts
per minute.

Calculation

$$\frac{\text{Disintegration rate injected}}{\text{Volume of blood}} = \frac{\text{Disintegration rate of sample}}{\text{Volume of sample}}$$

TASKS

a Select *two* procedures common to both
  methods. Account for the significance of
  each procedure. *(2)*
b On what general principle are both
  methods based? *(1)*
c Calculate the blood volume using both
  methods. *(2)*

Read the passage below and complete the tasks which follow.

Blood doping involves the removal of 1 litre of blood from an athlete, and its storage for about six weeks in a frozen state. The frozen blood is then thawed and returned (reinfused) to the athlete's bloodstream. During the time after removal of the blood, the athlete's body produces more red blood cells. After about five weeks, the number of red blood cells in the body has returned to normal. Haemoglobin within the red blood cells is the substance responsible for the transport of oxygen from the lungs to the muscles. The return of the blood (reinfusion) increases the total number of red blood cells and thus the amount of haemoglobin in the bloodstream. Studies have shown that after reinfusion, both the oxygen carrying capacity and endurance of the athlete are increased by 5 %. Such a difference can be the margin between success and failure. The graph shows the change in the percentage haemoglobin content of a volunteer after 1 litre of blood has been removed, stored for 8 weeks and reinfused. (A haemoglobin content of 100 % is normal.)

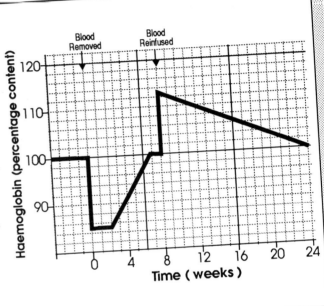

TASKS

a For an athlete, in which *two* ways does blood doping lead to an increase in muscle efficiency? *(1)*

b The oxygen carrying capacity of the volunteer is 70 cm³/kg/min before blood doping. What is the carrying capacity immediately after blood doping? *(1)*

c State *one* possible danger to the athlete associated with this technique. *(1)*

d Use the graph to answer the following:

1 How many weeks does it take for the haemoglobin content to return to normal after the removal of blood? *(1)*

2 What is the percentage increase in haemoglobin after reinfusion? *(1)*

3 How many weeks does it take for the haemoglobin content to return to normal after reinfusion? *(1)*

4 Account for the fact that athletes can not perform to the best of their ability during the period between blood removal and reinfusion. *(2)*

DOES FIT MEAN HEALTHY?

Evidence is growing that vigorous exercise is good for you. Professor Morris searched for a link between exercise and heart disease. He asked nearly 18 000 middle-aged men in the executive grade of the civil service, to supply details of their lifestyles. Over the following decade, he kept note of how many suffered heart attacks. Those men that had engaged in "vigorous exercise" were about half as likely to have experienced a heart attack as those who reported no vigorous exercise. High totals of physical activity were of some benefit, but intermittent peaks of high intensity apparently provided much greater protection against coronary heart disease. Benefits are that exercise can prevent or even reverse atherosclerosis, the disease in which fatty plaques build up in blood vessels. The plaques narrow the arteries that supply the muscle of the heart with blood. They reduce the supply of oxygen to the working muscle, and lead to chest pains, the death of part of the muscle, and disruptions in the rhythm of the heart beat. A high level of cholesterol in the blood is associated with a build up of these plaques.

So far, a direct effect of exercise on this disease has been demonstrated only in monkeys. A group of macaques were fed on a diet with added cholesterol and butter; some were then set to work on treadmills. The exercising monkeys developed larger hearts and cleaner arteries, while the sedentary ones showed a marked build up of plaque. Another possibility is that exercise, leading to enhanced "fitness", may protect the heart and help prevent disease by reducing the amount of oxygen the heart needs at any given level of exertion. The idea is that exercise has to be vigorous enough and for long enough, to produce what is known as a training effect. Long-term training for endurance decreases the rate at which the heart beats, both at rest and during exercise, so reducing the demand for oxygen from the heart muscle. Training increases the amount of blood that is pumped at each contraction. Athletes are also better at getting the blood through the veins and back to the heart. All these factors cause the heart muscle to stretch more as it is filling, giving the heart more force when it contracts.

TASKS

a Why would Professor Morris's results, from the civil servants, be statistically valid (lines 3–5)? *(1)*

b What conclusion does Morris come to about physical activity and the chance of heart attack (lines 9–12)? *(1)*

c Copy and complete the table to show the effect, on the heart, of a build-up of arterial fatty plaques (lines 15–19). *(2)*

Part of heart affected	Effect
Arteries to heart	
	Less oxygen
	Partial death of tissue
Tissue controlling contraction of muscle	

d How does the experiment with monkeys support the need for exercise (lines 24–27)? *(2)*

e Describe the form of exercise required to produce the *training effect* (line 32). *(1)*

f What is the benefit in reducing the rate of the heartbeat in long-term training (lines 32–35)? *(1)*

g What *two* factors lead to an increase in the volume of blood returning to an athlete's heart (lines 35–38)? *(1)*

h Explain how an increased volume of blood returning to the heart and a slower heartbeat combine to cause the heart muscle to stretch more as the heart fills (lines 38–40). *(3)*

6 INHERITANCE

1 BARLEY PLANTS

Ranu and Christopher carried out an investigation into the variation in height of barley plants in a field.

The results of both procedures are shown in the table.

Height interval (cm)	Number of plants	
	Ranu	**Christopher**
41–45	0	0
46–50	2	0
51–55	4	0
56–60	6	1
61–65	10	1
66–70	16	2
71–75	10	3
76–80	26	5
81–85	30	8
86–90	38	8
91–95	42	12
96–100	56	14
101–105	30	18
106–110	20	14
111–115	6	8
116–120	4	4
121–125	0	2

Ranu's procedure
—carried out on the 30th of July

1 The plants were taken from 20 randomly selected areas
2 The plants which were measured were selected at random
3 The heights of 15 plants were measured in each of the areas selected.

Christopher's procedure
—carried out on the 6th of August

1 The plants were taken from 20 randomly selected areas
2 The plants which were measured were selected at random
3 The heights of 5 plants were measured in each of the areas selected.

TASKS

a Using the data from Ranu's procedure, construct a histogram showing the number of plants in each height interval. *(3)*

b Combining the results from both sets of data:
  1 What height interval contains the greatest number of plants? *(1)*
  2 What percentage of plants has a height greater than 110 cm? *(1)*

c Why is it good experimental technique to select the plants at random? *(1)*

d Ranu concludes that the variation in height of barley plants is entirely genetically determined. Explain why this conclusion is probably wrong. *(1)*

e Explain how the date on which the measurements are taken in both procedures influences the results obtained. *(1)*

f Explain why Ranu's results are more reliable than Christophers in showing the variation in height of the plants. *(1)*

g In what *two* ways could the investigations be altered to ensure that a fair comparison of results is obtained? *(2)*

In a trout hatchery, all fertilised eggs are allowed to develop in the same controlled environment. Thus, any variation between individuals will be due mainly to genetic differences.

The table shows the number of young trout in each length interval, from a sample size of 500 hatched in 1987.

The following year, 1988, a sample of 250 trout was taken after the same period of growth as the previous year.

The number of trout in each length interval is shown in the histogram.

Number of young trout in the length interval	Length interval (cm)
0	7.0–7.4
0	7.5–7.9
9	8.0–8.4
16	8.5–8.9
51	9.0–9.4
105	9.5–9.9
115	10.0–10.4
84	10.5–10.9
41	11.0–11.4
49	11.5–11.9
16	12.0–12.4
10	12.5–12.9
4	13.0–13.4
0	13.5–13.9

Year 1988
Sample size 250

TASKS

a Using the table, construct a histogram showing variation in length of trout within the sample population (use the scales shown in the histogram). (2)

b What percentage of the trout were between 9.5–9.9 cm in length in 1987? (1)

c Which of the two years has the widest range in trout length? (1)

d Name *two* factors which should be kept constant in the environment if a fair comparison of variation in lengths is to be made between the two samples. (2)

e Apart from environmental differences, what factor in the procedure makes any comparison between the samples unreliable? (1)

f What percentage of trout in the 1988 sample have a length of more than 11.9 cm? (1)

g Express as a ratio the difference in the number present in the length intervals 8.5–8.9 cm as seen in the two years. (1)

3 DOMINANT AND RECESSIVE

Examine the following table showing a number
of crosses and the phenotypes produced.

| Cross | Parents in cross | | Phenotypes produced |
	Parent A	Parent B	
1	Tall pea plants	× Dwarf pea plants	All tall
2	Normal-winged fruit flies	× Normal-winged fruit flies	Normal winged Dumpy winged
3	Grey-bodied fruit flies	× Ebony-bodied fruit flies	Grey bodied Ebony bodied
4	Tall pea plants	× Dwarf pea plants	20 tall and 20 dwarf pea plants
5	Wrinkle-seeded pea plants	× Round-seeded pea plants	80 round-seeded pea plants
6	Purple-stemmed tomato plants	× Purple-stemmed tomato plants	120 purple-stemmed tomato plants

TASK

Select from the list of statements, using the
appropriate letter, the statement which
applies to the parents in each cross in the
table. (**Note:** Each letter can be used once,
more than once, or not at all.) (6)

Letter	List of statements
P	The dominant characteristic is shown only in the phenotype of parent A
Q	The dominant characteristic is shown only in the phenotype of parent B
R	The dominant characteristic is shown in the phenotype of both parents A and B
S	The recessive characteristic is shown only in the phenotype of parent A
T	The recessive characteristic is shown only in the phenotype of parent B
U	The cross shown does not allow the dominant and recessive characteristics to be identified.

4   TONGUE ROLLERS

The ability to roll the tongue is genetically inherited. People either have or do not have the ability to be a 'roller'.

Richard carried out an investigation to find out if there was a difference between the numbers of boys and girls who were 'rollers'. In his investigation Richard tested 120 boys and 100 girls. Of the boys 102 were 'rollers' and of the girls 80 were 'rollers'.

TASKS

a What percentage of boys tested are *rollers*? *(1)*
b From his results, Richard calculates that a greater percentage of boys than of girls in the sample are *rollers*. Richard concludes that in the human population, more boys than girls are *rollers*.
  1 Explain how Richard's procedure makes this conclusion unreliable. *(1)*
  2 Suggest how the reliability of his results could be improved. *(1)*

5   PHENOTYPES

Examine the following crosses and complete the tasks which follow.

A Pea plants

Cross	Parents	Offspring
1	Tall × Dwarf	F1 100 plants tall only
2	Tall × Tall (F1) (F1)	F2 78 tall 26 dwarf
3	Tall × Dwarf (F1)	F2 51 tall 48 dwarf

B Fruit flies

Cross	Parents	Offspring
1	Normal × Dumpy winged winged	F1 150 flies (normal)
2	Normal × Normal winged winged (F1) (F1)	F2 111 normal 37 dumpy
3	Normal × Dumpy winged winged (F1)	F2 74 normal 76 dumpy

TASKS

a What appears to be the common pattern in the phenotypes produced in cross 1 in *A* and *B*? *(1)*
b What appears to be the common pattern between the numbers of the phenotypes produced in:
  1 cross 2 in *A* and *B*
  2 cross 3 in *A* and *B*? *(2)*

c Which parents from cross 1 in *A* and *B* can be described as
  1 true-breeding
  2 having the dominant phenotype? *(2)*
d Which parents from cross 3 in *A* and *B* can be described as being both true-breeding and recessive? *(1)*

6 CHROMOSOMES

The diagrams below show the matched sets of chromosomes in two humans A and B.

Individual A possesses the *normal* chromosome number and complement.

Individual B possesses an *abnormal* chromosome number and complement.

Individual A

Individual B

TASKS

a State, giving a reason, which individual is male and which is female. *(2)*

b What is the chromosome *number* of individual B? *(1)*

c How does the chromosome *complement* of individual B differ from that of individual A? *(1)*

7 DOWN'S SYNDROME

Children with Down's syndrome are readily identifiable from their appearance. The effects of the disorder are unfortunately both mental and physical, however, the degree of severity varies with the individual. Life expectancy used to be
5 short. The children died from infections, heart defects and were susceptible to leukaemia. Nowadays, with the use of drugs and heart surgery, these children live much longer. The more common type of Down's syndrome is caused by failure of the chromosome pair 21 to separate during formation of
10 the egg. The egg, with two of chromosome 21, is then fertilised by a normal sperm. The Down's syndrome child has, therefore, three of chromosome 21, instead of two, a condition known as trisomy 21. The chromosome complement of the child is 47 instead of 46.

The graph shows the relationship between the age of the mother and the risk of having a Down's syndrome baby.

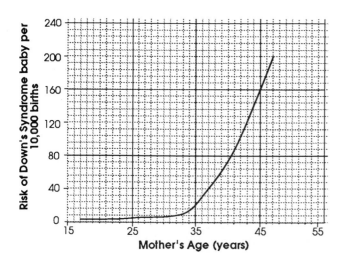

Mother's Age (years)

Risk of Down's Syndrome baby per 10,000 births

TASKS

a Name *two* causes of the short life expectancy in Down's syndrome children. *(1)*

b Which *two* forms of treatment have extended the life expectancy for Down's syndrome children? *(1)*

c How many chromosomes are present in an egg which develops, after fertilisation, into a baby with Down's syndrome? *(1)*

d What is meant by *trisomy 21* (line 13)? *(1)*

e From the graph:

  1 State the relationship between the mother's age and the chance of having a baby with Down's syndrome. *(1)*

  2 State the expected number of babies with Down's syndrome, in 10 000 births from 45-year-old mothers. *(1)*

  3 By how many times does the risk of having a baby with Down's syndrome increase, between 37 and 47 years of age? *(1)*

8 BETA THALASSAEMIA

A single gene is responsible for the inherited disorder, beta thalassaemia, in humans.

Read the passage below and complete the tasks which follow.

GRIM PRICE TO PAY FOR THE FACE OF PETER PAN

George Coustantinou wouldn't get a drink from the most lax of barmen. Yet George is 30 years old. His youthful appearance is a by-product of treatments that have saved his life.

5 He is an adult survivor of the deadly blood disorder- *beta thalassaemia*. This condition, carried by symptomless individuals, causes victims to be born without proper red blood cells to carry oxygen.

Monthly transfusions can save them, although these, in
10 turn, cause blood-borne iron to accumulate in the heart and kidneys, leading to death in late adolescence. Recently, however, the drug 'desferal', which removes iron from the body - has given them the prospect of extended life.

15 Doctors have also learned how to pinpoint affected foetuses, so parents can be offered abortions. In Cyprus, Sardinia and mainland Italy, this has led to a virtual halt in *thalassaemia* births.

A major priority for affected patients is the development
20 of a 'desferal' substitute that could be taken orally. 'We have to use pumps 10 hours a day to administer "desferal" intravenously,' said George. 'They are bulky, obvious, and make us feel different. A simple pill would make us human beings again.'

25 Ultimately, the only real solution is a full cure for *thalassaemia*.

Only gene therapy will achieve that goal, probably using genetically-engineered viruses to carry genes for haemoglobin, the crucial component of red blood cells, into a
30 patient's bone marrow, where blood cells grow. There the missing genes will hopefully 'take root' and begin to make life-giving haemoglobin.

Observer

TASKS

a What evidence suggests that the treatment for beta thalassaemia retards physical development? *(1)*

b Explain how the fact, that this condition is *carried by symptomless individuals*, tells you that the condition is inherited as a recessive characteristic (lines 6–7). *(2)*

c What *two* treatments are given to beta thalassaemia patients to enable them to survive beyond adolescence (lines 9–14)? *(2)*

d Why is it necessary to remove iron from the bodies of these patients (lines 9–14)? *(1)*

e Account for the *virtual halt in thalassaemia births* in Italy (lines 15–18). *(2)*

f What *two* reasons are given to explain why patients see *development of a 'desferal' substitute that could be taken orally* as a major priority (lines 19–24)? *(2)*

g Account for the fact that diagnosis of beta thalassaemia involves examination of the patient's blood. *(1)*

h Describe how genetic engineering could lead to a cure for beta thalassaemia (lines 27–32). *(3)*

9 BST AND MILK

Read the passage below and complete the tasks which follow.

Bovine somatotrophin (BST) is a growth hormone. Injected into cows, it increases the production of milk, partly by diverting a large proportion of her food from ordinary
5 metabolism into milk production. The cow then eats more fodder and continues to turn more of it into milk. Fears over human health risks are not an issue. BST is present in the milk of all cows, whether treated or
10 not. The bovine version of the hormone is inactive in humans and is broken down in the gut. Large quantities of BST became available when genetic engineers inserted the gene for BST into bacteria. Studies have
15 shown that cows give up to 41% *more milk* when injected daily with BST during the later part of the lactation period, when yields are usually declining. The increased milk production during a complete period of
20 lactation varies from 10% to 25%. Large variations in milk yield were found also to result from the way in which herds are managed. In herds which are managed in the best possible way, the milk yield is limited
25 by the genetic potential of the cows, and these cows will not respond greatly to BST. This is not surprising, because high-yielding cows were selected for their own, high, production of BST in the first place. The side
30 effects of high levels of BST on the cow are a higher incidence of infection, lower fertility and more heat stress. BST mimics the cows physiology at the beginning of a cycle of lactation. At that time, a cow is normally
35 more susceptible to infection.

TASKS

a Account for the fact that when treated with BST, the cow's food intake has to be increased (line 6). (2)

b Give *two* reasons why this growth hormone is *not* viewed as a danger to human health (line 8). (2)

c Explain how *large quantities of BST became available* (lines 12–13). (2)

d Why does BST treatment, at the later part of the lactation period, have greatest effect on milk yield (lines 14–18)? (1)

e If a cow has a milk yield of 3500 litres per annum, calculate the greatest increase in milk yield that could be predicted, when using BST treatment (lines 14–20). (1)

f What factor other than hormone treatment has a great influence on milk yield? (1)

g Explain how selective breeding removes the need for BST treatment. (2)

h Select *two* disadvantages of using BST treatment. (1)

This first appeared in New Scientist

10 WILD POTATOES

All of Europe's potato varieties of the common potato, are derived from a single species, *Solanum tuberosum*. Two samples were brought to Spain in about 1570 and it was clones from these which were introduced to England and
5 then to Ireland. In 1846, there occurred the Irish potato famine in which the blight fungus, *Phyophthora infestans*, spread through the genetically-similar Irish potatoes, devastating the crop. Approximately 263 pests and diseases attack potatoes. The 128 insects, 68 eelworms,
10 38 fungi, 23 viruses and 6 bacteria that damage potatoes, occasionally mutate and become more of a problem. *Solanum demissum*, from Mexico, was found to resist late blight and the responsible gene was bred into the common potato. Unfortunately, gains from a single gene are usually
15 short-lived. As a general rule breeders try to incorporate multiple-gene resistance for longer protection. Bacteria can trigger numerous ailments but *Solanum chacoense*, a wild variety, contains genes coding for resistance to bacteria. From the range of viruses that can plague
20 potatoes, *Solanum acaule* survives infection by potato virus X, a disease of the common potato. Eelworms tunnel into the roots however *Solanum vernei* was found to offer resistance to such attacks. Gene banks are also indispensable to breeders faced with the challenge of producing
25 potatoes that thrive on poor soils and can withstand severe climates. High-altitude species from the Andes, such as *Solanum curtilobum*, withstand frost and so have been added to the gene bank.

Adapted from New Scientist

TASKS

a Describe *one* danger to growing crops which are genetically identical (lines 1–8). (1)

b Construct a bar chart to show the number of pests and pathogens which attack potatoes (lines 8–12). (3)

c From the information in lines 12–28, construct a table, using suitable headings, to show the advantages of the named varieties. (3)

d Explain the importance to breeders of the conservation of areas in which wild varieties, such as *Solanum chacoense*, occur (line 17). (2)

e Explain why breeders carry out multiple-gene transfer between varieties in preference to single-gene transfer (lines 15–16). (2)

f Name the varieties available to a breeder if he wishes to incorporate resistance to late blight and frost in the common potato (lines 12–28). (2)

11

Cross	Dominant characteristic	Recessive characteristic	Description of parents in cross
1	Horns in cattle	Hornless in cattle	Heterozygous × Hornless horned
2	Grey-bodied fruit flies	Ebony-bodied fruit flies	Heterozygous × Heterozygous grey-bodied grey-bodied
3	Red-flowering plants	White-flowering plants	White × White flowering flowering
4	Round-seeded plants	Wrinkle-seeded plants	Wrinkle × Homozygous seeded round seeded

Examine each of the crosses in the table on the opposite page and then complete the task below.

TASK

Select from the list of possible phenotype ratios, using the appropriate letter, the expected ratio produced in each cross. (**Note:** Each letter can be used once, more than once, or not at all.) *(4)*

Letter	Possible phenotype ratios
P	100 % dominant characteristic
Q	75 % dominant and 25 % recessive characteristic
R	50 % dominant and 50 % recessive characteristic
S	100 % recessive characteristic

12

In humans, one of the genes which affects eye colour has three different alleles. Homozygous combinations of these alleles produce the following phenotypes:
● B1B1—brown eyes
● B2B2—hazel eyes
● bb —blue eyes.

The alleles show complete dominance in the order:
● B1 dominant to B2
● B2 dominant to b.

Study the family tree below showing eye colour and answer the questions which follow.

TASKS

a Identify the genotype of
 1 Margaret
 2 Ewan
 3 Mhari
 4 Donald. *(2)*
b If Angus and Mhari have another child, what are the chances of its eye colour being hazel? *(1)*
c Which individuals are homozygous? *(1)*
d Explain why Morag's genotype cannot be identified from this information. *(1)*

Family tree

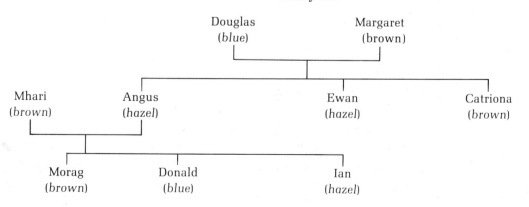

13 DEER FARMING

Read the passage and complete the tasks which follow.

Although red deer farming is a success, it has not worked out quite as well as expected. Red deer have two inherent drawbacks. They do not grow as quickly as desired. By the end of
5 their second summer, calves may not have reached 80 kg slaughter weight, or hinds the required breeding weight of 80 kg. Red deer give birth in June. This means that calves are hard pressed to reach 40 kg by weaning time
10 in September, from an average birth weight of 8 kg. Growth rate falls after they are weaned onto their winter feed and unless they have reached 40 kg at weaning, they are unlikely to reach slaughter weight by the end of the
15 following summer. If they are left with the hind to maintain a high growth rate, she will not be ready for mating in October.
There are two ways to overcome the late-
breeding problem. The first is to adjust the
20 breeding cycles of the red deer by dosing them with the hormone melatonin. Melatonin is produced naturally in response to changing daylength. Doses of melatonin enable the hind to become pregnant in September and to give
25 birth in early May.
The second approach is to cross red deer with a species of deer that breeds earlier. Pere David's deer, native to China, are early breeders, thrive anywhere and grow large so that by
30 slaughtering time at the end of the second summer, they have reached 160 kg. In addition, the wapiti, a native of North America, can be crossed with red deer. The wapiti has the same breeding season as the red deer but it
35 grows to the same size as Pere David's deer.

Adapted from New Scientist

TASKS

a What are the *two* inherent drawbacks of using red deer for commercial purposes (line 3)? (2)

b Calculate the average monthly gain in weight of an average red deer calf, from birth in June to weaning in September, when its weight has reached 40 kg (lines 8–11). (1)

c By how many times does the weight of a red deer calf have to increase from the time of birth to the time of slaughter (lines 4–6)? (1)

d State *two* ways of overcoming the late-breeding problem (lines 18–19). (2)

e If a calf has not reached 40 kg by weaning time what are the consequences to the deer farmer if he
  1 continues to let it feed from the hind
  2 weans the calf (lines 11–13)? (2)

f Which environmental factor triggers the start of the breeding cycle? (1)

g What *two* advantages may be gained by crossing red deer with Pere David's deer (lines 26–31)? (2)

h Explain how the fact that the wapiti deer have the same late-breeding season as red deer does not prevent their use in selective breeding (line 35). (1)

BLOOD GROUPS

The gene which determines the human blood groups 0, A, B, and AB follows a Mendelian inheritance. There are three different alleles of this gene and they are usually shown by the symbols IA, IB and i. (IA and IB are both dominant to i.) Dominant genes cause a characteristic to be expressed and, in blood groups, IA and IB are both dominant. IA determines the production of factor A in the blood and IB determines the production of factor B. An individual with the genotype IAIB produces factor A and factor B and their blood group is described as being of phenotype group AB. The frequency of each allele in a population can be calculated. The frequency includes those individuals who carry both alleles for the same gene or who carry only one of the alleles. Thus the frequency of the allele i includes not only individuals who are ii, but also those who are IAi or IBi. The frequency of each allele for a blood group varies among different human populations. The table shows the frequency of each allele for some populations.

	Percentage frequency of allele		
Population	i	IA	IB
Scots	72	21	7
Irish	74	19	7
English	68	26	6
Hindus	55	18	26
Chinese	59	22	20

TASK

a Use the information given to copy and complete the table of genotypes and phenotypes of the various blood groups. *(3)*

Genotypes	Phenotypes
IAIA	Group – – –
– – – i	Group A
– – – – – –	Group AB
IBIB	Group – – –
IB– – – or IB– – –	Group B
– – – – – –	Group O

TASKS

b Use the table to construct a bar chart showing the percentage frequency of each of the alleles in the populations. *(3)*

c Express as a ratio (to the nearest whole number) the difference in the percentage frequency of each allele in the Scots. *(1)*

d From the frequency of alleles in the Scots population state which blood group would be
　1 most common within the population
　2 second most common within the population
　3 least common within the population. *(2)*

SICKLE CELL ANAEMIA

The dominant allele, HbA, controls the production of normal haemoglobin. Haemoglobin transports oxygen to the tissues, and is required for cells to function normally. The recessive allele, HbS, controls production of abnormal haemoglobin, type-S. In a homozygous recessive individual, HbSHbS, all of the haemoglobin is type-S and this causes red blood cells to have a sickle shape at normal oxygen levels. The result is severe and usually fatal anaemia (sickle-cell anaemia). Heterozygotes, HbAHbS, are healthy but some may show signs of the trait, especially when oxygen levels are low. That the abnormal allelle has survived at a high frequency, is related to the fact that the heterozygous condition enables the individual to survive the effects of malaria better than normal homozygotes. The heterozygotes that survive will breed and pass on the allele for the trait, to the next generation. The recessive allele originated in the malarial areas of Africa, however, it is still present among the negro communities in America.

Summary

HbA/HbA Normal phenotype susceptible to malaria.
HbA/HbS Normal phenotype resistant to malaria.
Hbs/HbS Anaemic phenotype usually dies.

Below is a typical pedigree showing sickle cell anaemia.

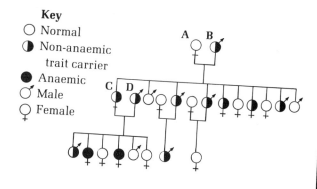

Key
○ Normal
◐ Non-anaemic trait carrier
● Anaemic
♂ Male
♀ Female

TASKS

a Dental anaesthetics lower the oxygen level of the blood. Explain why such treatment is dangerous for an individual who is heterozygous for sickle-cell anaemia. *(2)*

b Explain how, in a malarial area, heterozygotes for sickle-cell anaemia are selected for survival. *(2)*

c Why, in a non-malarial area, is the expected occurrence of the sickle-cell allele in a population low? *(2)*

d Give the genotype ratio of the offspring from couple A and B in the pedigree. How does this ratio differ from the expected ratio? *(2)*

e 1 What is the expected genotype ratio obtained from a cross between two individuals, of the same genotype as C and D in the pedigree? *(1)*

2 Account for the fact that the ratio obtained, as shown in the cross, differs from the expected ratio. *(1)*

Evolution of an inherited disease

PHENYLKETONURIA (PKU) is one of the commonest genetic disorders that is inherited recessively among northern Europeans. It is caused by a defect in the gene that codes for the enzyme
5 phenylalanine hydroxylase. People with two copies of the mutated gene do not produce the enzyme and become mentally retarded unless they eat a diet free of phenylalanine. Children born in Britain are routinely tested for the disor-
10 der at birth, by a simple biochemical blood test. Now, researchers in Houston, Texas, have identified two mutations that together account for half the cases in people of northern European origin. The discovery makes it possible to screen the
15 genetic material of adults to identify 90 per cent of the people who are carriers of the disorder. The discovery also sheds light on the evolutionary origins of the disease. It is surprising that a genetic disorder as common as PKU can be
20 traced back to just a handful of mutational events. Before the new research, geneticists suspected that PKU is common because the gene mutates at a high rate. But Anthony DiLella and his colleagues at Baylor College of Medicine,

25 have shown that more than half the people with PKU are directly descended from two people who experienced the initial mutations. Such evidence suggests that being a carrier (heterozygous) might now be, or in the past have been, ad-
30 vantageous in some unknown way, allowing the mutated genes to spread through the population by "balancing selection".

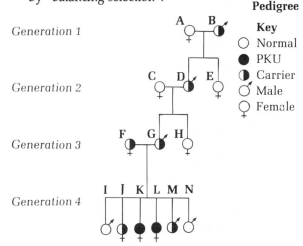

Adapted from New Scientist

TASKS

a What is the main theme of the passage? *(1)*

b What phrase from the passage means that a person is true-breeding and recessive for phenylketonuria (PKU)? *(1)*

c Describe:
  1 the effect of the disorder
  2 how it is detected
  3 how its effect is prevented. *(2)*

d Explain why it is important to identify *people who are carriers of the disorder* (lines 15–16). *(2)*

e Why were researchers surprised *that more than half the people with PKU ....the initial mutation* (lines 25–27)? *(1)*

f Explain why the term *carrier* is an accurate description of the heterozygote (line 28). *(2)*

g What evidence from the pedigree supports the statement that PKU *is inherited recessively* (line 2)? *(1)*

h How does the ratio obtained in Generation 4 differ from that expected? *(2)*

i What are the chances of individual M being heterozygous? *(1)*

1 BREWING BEER

In the manufacture of beer, sugars are converted to alcohol and carbon dioxide by the fermentation action of yeast. The increase in carbon dioxide produced, causes a change in pH. During the process of fermentation some of the energy is lost as heat.

In an investigation into beer-making, a pupil carried out the following procedure:
1 The ingredients were placed in a brew bucket, together with a sachet of yeast
2 The temperature of the brew, the room temperature and the pH of the beer were monitored using three sensors, over a 7 day period
3 The results are shown on the graph.

a Account for the change in pH during the investigation. (2)
b How many hours does it take for the initial pH value to decrease by one unit? (1)
c State the relationship between room temperature and brew bucket temperature. (1)
d Account for the fact that the temperature of the brew bucket always remain above the room temperature. (2)
e How does the graph of the change in pH support the statement that the rate of fermentation slows with time? (1)

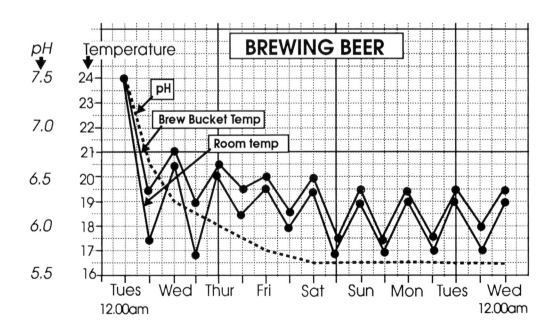

2 LOW-ALCOHOL BEER

Guardian

Alcohol-free and low alcohol beer brewers can hardly contain their excitement. There are now more than 30 brands of low-alcohol and no-alcohol beer. Growth in sales so far has been achieved only with hugely-expensive advertising.

5 About £80 million a year is spent promoting "ordinary" beer—the equivalent of about 1p a pint. This year's advertising budget for low and no-alcohol beers, involving hunky characters like Ian Botham, Billy Connolly and Lenny Henry to help dispel the wimpy "boys' beer" image, will cost around £15 million — about

10 17p a pint.

Most alcohol-free (less than 0.05 per cent alcohol) and low alcohol (usually between 0.5 and 1.0 per cent) beers are brewed in the conventional way, then alcohol is taken out. The idea is simple. Make a full-strength lager. Warm it slightly and

15 put the brew in a partial vacuum. Most alcohol is driven off because at low pressure it boils at a lower temperature.

A variation is to force a beer through a membrane. Alcohol and water go through the membrane more easily than the larger molecules which are effectively beer concentrate. Add water and

20 you have a low-alcohol beer.

But both processes mean some change in flavour. The newer approach is to stop too much alcohol being produced in the first place.

There are three ways of doing this:

25 • by chilling the yeast before it has made much alcohol;
• put in less fermentable carbohydrate for the yeast to work on;
• find a yeast with little enthusiasm for making alcohol.

It is this third avenue which brewing industry scientists believe to be most promising. They are experimenting with genetic engi-

30 neering to create a new strain of yeast to make a driver-friendly and liver-friendly brew which tastes like the real thing.

TASKS

a What is the difference between alcohol-free and low-alcohol beers? *(1)*

b How much more per pint is spent on advertising low and alcohol-free beers than on ordinary beer (lines 5–10)? *(1)*

c Given that an alcohol-free beer contains 0.05% alcohol, calculate how many times greater the range of alcohol content is, in most low-alcohol beers (lines 11–13). *(1)*

d From the passage select *one* example of
  1 a social advantage
  2 a health advantage
  of people switching to low and alcohol-free beers. *(2)*

e Copy and complete the table below to show the details of different techniques for the production of low and alcohol-free beers (lines 14–27). *(3)*

Technique for producing low and alcohol-free beers	Details of technique
Evaporation in vacuum	
	Water and alcohol pass through more easily than beer flavouring components
Chilling	
Low carbohydrate brew	
	This yeast converts little of the sugar to alcohol

3 YOGHURT

Yoghurt manufacture depends on the action, on milk, of several types of bacteria. The ideal temperature for yoghurt manufacture is 40 °C. Two types of bacteria act together to cause the milk to thicken and go sour. The sourness is due to the conversion of lactose sugar in the milk to lactic acid. When the correct level of acidity, taste and consistency is reached, the yoghurt is cooled. This slows down the bacterial activity but does not kill the bacteria. The lactic acid and low pH prevent the growth of other bacterial species.

In an investigation into yoghurt manufacture, a pupil carried out the following procedure:

1 A water bath was set at 40 °C
2 200 cm³ of sterilised milk was placed in a sterile beaker and 5 cm³ of *live* yoghurt was added to the milk
3 The mixture was stirred and placed in the water bath
4 The temperature and pH were monitored, by two sensors, over a 3 hour period
5 The results are shown in the graph.

TASKS

a Account for the slope of the graph between A and B. (2)
b Account for the change in pH shown on the graph. (2)
c What is the pH of the milk at the start of the investigation? (1)
d Why is it important to use sterilised milk in the investigation? (1)
e Explain why yoghurt should be stored at a low temperature rather than at room temperature. (2)
f What control experiment should be set up in order to validate the results obtained? (1)
g How could you demonstrate that 40 °C was the ideal temperature for yoghurt manufacture? (2)
h Predict what results would be obtained if the investigation was repeated with 10 cm³ of *live* yoghurt being added to 200 cm³ of milk. (1)

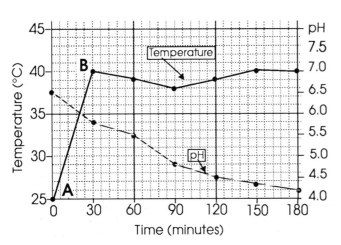

4 COOK-CHILL FOOD

Read the passage below and complete the tasks which follow.

COOK-CHILL

Professor Richard Lacey of Leeds University believes the cook-chill process may be to blame for 150 deaths in hospitals every year. The method involves preparing a large quantity of
5 food in a factory; chilling it very rapidly to 3 degrees Centigrade; transporting it in refrigerated lorries to its destination and reheating it for eating. Professor Lacey claims that although
10 airlines have been serving cook-chilled meals for many years, this process is not suitable for hospital patients, whose immune systems are often deficient. The Professor also fears that competitive tendering may lead to poor quality
15 ingredients being used, which are more likely to remain contaminated throughout the cook-chill process. The advantage of cook-chill in hospitals is that meals are hot because they are served from oven trolleys in wards. "However, bacteria
20 which produce toxins are not killed below 100°C and the trolleys' final temperature is 70°C," said Professor Lacey. He believes that cook-chill's effect can be traced through the recent increase in cases of listeriosis - 259 in 1987, com-
25 pared with 107 in 1986. The listeria organism, unlike salmonella, multiplies in refrigerators and is resistant to heat. While salmonella develops within 48 hours and is usually not deadly, listeriosis takes up to a month to incubate and has a 30
30 percent death rate, he says. The Institution of Environmental Health Officers believes hospital food has improved since the introduction of cook-chill and the system is potentially safer than older catering methods.

Guardian

TASKS

a Give a description of the cook-chill process (lines 3−9). *(3)*

b How would Professor Lacey argue the fact, that although cook-chill meals have been used for many years by airlines, they are *not* suitable for hospital patients (lines 9−12)? *(1)*

c What are the professor's concerns over
  1 the use of poor quality ingredients (lines 13−17) *(1)*
  2 the final temperature of oven trolleys being 70 °C (lines 17−22)? *(1)*

d Calculate the approximate percentage increase in listeriosis from 1986 to 1987 (lines 22−25). *(1)*

e What *two* reasons does the professor give for thinking that listeria is more likely to be present in cook-chill food than is salmonella (lines 25−27)? *(2)*

f Explain why an infection caused by listeria is potentially more dangerous than one caused by salmonella (lines 27−30). *(1)*

g What *two* reasons are given by the Institute of Environmental Health Officers for their support of the cook-chill system (lines 30−34)? *(2)*

SEWAGE TREATMENT

The main methods of sewage treatment, used today, rely on the breakdown of the organic material in sewage by bacteria, in the presence of oxygen from the air.

Before treatment, the sewage is first passed through a screen of iron bars, to prevent large objects entering the works. Grit and stones are allowed to settle in a grit separator and the sewage then flows into primary settlement tanks. The large particles of sewage settle to the bottom of the tanks and are removed as a sludge, while the liquid at the top flows on, for the biological oxidation step. In the percolating filter process, the

liquid is sprayed by rotating radial arms over a large tank filled with stones which are about 5 cm in diameter. The stones are covered with a variety of biological life and can be regarded as a balanced ecosystem. There is a slime which consists chiefly of bacteria and these feed on the organic matter in the sewage. Insect larvae and worms are also present and feed on the bacterial slime. Some of the insect larvae metamorphose into flies and these are caught by birds.

The liquid which is collected at the base of the filter tank contains the breakdown products of the organic matter. These particles are allowed to settle in a final settling tank while the clean overflow water is discharged as effluent to the river. The diagram shows the flow of sewage through a percolating filter works with the connecting lines and arrows omitted.

Few pollution problems should result from a good quality sewage effluent discharge. The oxygen required for the oxidation of any organic matter remaining in the discharge, is removed from the river water by bacteria. This results in a slight decrease in the oxygen concentration of a river downstream of an effluent outfall. The results in the table show the effect, on clean river water, of a discharge of good quality sewage effluent.

Chemicals present	Chemical analysis (mg/litres)		
	Effluent from sewage works	Clean river upstream	River downstream of effluent
Dissolved oxygen	7.1	10.3	9.9
Ammoniacal nitrogen	13.5	0.6	0.8
Nitrate nitrogen	0.7	1.3	1.8
Phosphate phosphorus	1.0	0.3	0.4
Detergent	0.8	Nil	0.1

a What *two* factors are necessary for the breakdown of organic material in sewage? *(1)*

b How is a large surface area for bacterial action created in the percolating filter process? *(1)*

c Copy and complete the diagram, by means of connecting arrows, to show the flow of material through a percolating sewage works. *(3)*

d Using the information in paragraph 2, construct a food web of the organisms mentioned. Use organic matter in the sewage as the initial food source. *(3)*

e What evidence from the table suggests, that the ammoniacal nitrogen in the effluent is converted to nitrates by bacteria? *(2)*

f From the table calculate the percentage increase in phosphate phosphorus in the river, downstream from the effluent. *(1)*

g The table shows an oxygen decrease of approximately 4 % after the addition of effluent. What explanation is given for this decrease? *(1)*

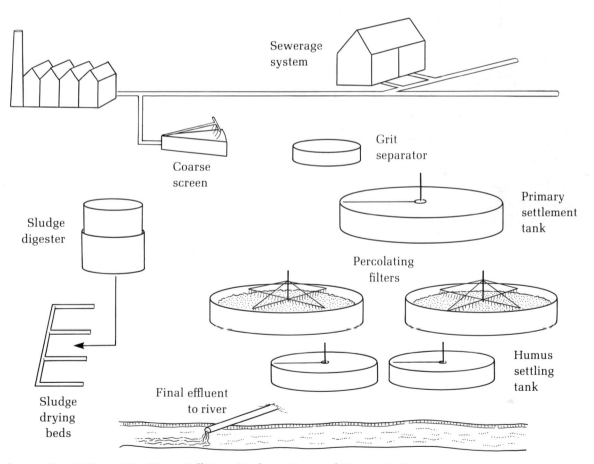

Source: Best & Ross 1977, 'River Pollution Studies'. Liverpool University Press

6 SALMONELLA IN EGGS

Read the passage below and complete the tasks which follow.

We exercise double standards in this country. Food factories and restaurants are subject to strict hygiene regulations, but farmers are exempt, said Mr Alan Thompson, of the Institution of Environmental Health
5 Officers. Mr Thompson was speaking in the wake of the controversy started by Edwina Currie when she claimed that most of the egg production in this country sadly is now infected by salmonella.
More than 12,000 cases of *Salmonella enteritidis*, a type
10 of salmonella almost exclusively associated with poultry and eggs, have been reported this year, a large proportion of which may have been due to the consumption of lightly cooked or raw eggs. Food poisoning is seriously under-reported and many
15 experts say the total number can be multiplied by 10.
A survey of 84 chicken-feed processing plants showed that in 21 cases, the feed was contaminated. But no prosecutions followed. Many want to see a complete ban on the feeding of animal products to
20 chickens, to stamp out the circular chain of infection. Such feeding practices are banned in Denmark where the problem of salmonella is much less.
Government guidelines, which recommend that farmers buy only salmonella-free chicks and use only
25 salmonella-free feed, are currently only a code of practice and have no legal status. Dr Mead, a researcher, has been working on the theory that salmonella flourishes in the gut of chicks, because intensive rearing methods mean the chicks are
30 deprived of other natural microbiological flora, which would normally compete with the salmonella. In a long-term experiment, he has introduced a range of gut microbes to 22 flocks and succeeded in keeping salmonella out of 20 of them.

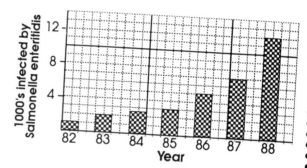

Observer

TASKS

a What fact led Mr Alan Thompson to relate the increase in salmonella food poisoning to *double standards* (lines 1–5)? *(1)*

b The number of people affected by salmonella food poisoning is difficult to calculate exactly. Using the data from lines 9–15, produce a figure which many experts consider to be close to the truth. *(1)*

c Account for the fact that infection is blamed on the *consumption of lightly cooked or raw eggs* (lines 9–13). *(2)*

d What percentage of chicken-feed processing plants visited in 1987 produced feed which was contaminated with salmonella (lines 16–17)? *(1)*

e What evidence supports a complete ban on *the feeding of animal products to chickens* (lines 18–22)? *(1)*

f Explain how each of the *two* recommendations laid down in the government guidelines, reduces the incidence of salmonella food poisoning (lines 23–26). *(2)*

g Describe how the application of Dr Mead's theory helps in the reduction of salmonella food poisoning (lines 26–34). *(2)*

h Using the data from the bar chart, express as a ratio the difference in the number of people affected by *Salmonella enteritidis* in 1982 and 1988. *(1)*

7   THE RUBBISH TIP

According to the latest thinking on waste management in Britain, the future of landfill rests squarely on treating the tip as a natural process plant, a large-scale bioreactor. What happens in a tip is simple. After the rubbish is
5 dumped, compressed and covered, the organic material is starved of oxygen and attacked by bacteria. This is known as anaerobic digestion. Ultimately, a methane-rich gas (landfill gas) results, two-thirds methane and one-third carbon dioxide. Landfill gas can be collected
10 and used as a source of low-grade energy. The gas can also be a hazard. Uncontrolled, it can travel large distances, get into buildings and even cause explosions. The dumps also hold acidic liquids, which are generated as material in the dump decomposes. These are a threat
15 to wildlife and water supplies. Tips should be engineered to maximise the production and collection of landfill gas. This will require research on a large scale into the effect of plastics on gas generation. The waste industry will also need to develop techniques to control
20 the moisture level and temperature of a tip. Tip operators also need to be able to monitor the microbiological conditions inside the tip. The new breed of tip will hold the rubbish between synthetic liners which will sit above, around and below the tip. The tip would be
25 capped with an impermeable membrane. Gas would then be collected by pumping it from wells.

Adapted from New Scientist

TASKS

a Describe the process of anaerobic digestion, by which methane and carbon dioxide are produced in rubbish tips (lines 4–9). *(2)*

b State *two* environmental dangers associated with the production of landfill gas (lines 11–15). *(2)*

c Knowledge of the ways in which a tip functions is incomplete. List *two* areas, suggested for further research, which could help improve tip management (lines 17–20). *(2)*

d Which *two* environmental factors mentioned affect the *microbiological conditions inside the tip* (lines 21–22)? *(1)*

e Describe how gas from the tip could be contained and extracted (lines 22–26). *(2)*

8 BIOGAS

Plant and other organic waste materials can be used as a food source by microorganisms. If this process is carried out in the absence of oxygen a mixture of the gases methane (biogas) and carbon dioxide is produced. Biogas is an energy source and it can be used as a substitute for coal and North Sea gas.

Pratima and John carried out an investigation to find out if chicken manure is a better producer of biogas than compost. Both used the apparatus shown in the diagram.

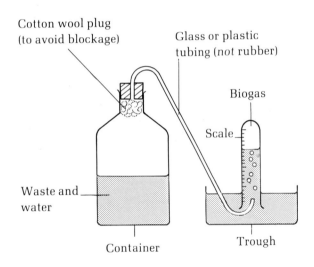

Cotton wool plug (to avoid blockage)

Glass or plastic tubing (*not* rubber)

Biogas

Scale

Waste and water

Container

Trough

Results

Time (hours)	Volume reading (cm³)	Volume produced per hour (cm³)
0	0	0
1	1	1
2	3	2
3	7	4
4	15	8
5	31	16

John's procedure
1 100 g of dried compost were mixed with 1 litre of distilled water and placed in the container
2 The container was placed in a water-bath at 35 °C
3 The volume of gas produced each hour was measured over a period of 5 hours.

Results

Time (hours)	Volume reading (cm³)	Volume produced per hour (cm³)
0	0.0	0.0
1	0.5	0.5
2	1.5	1.0
3	3.5	2.0
4	7.5	4.0
5	15.5	8.0

Pratima's procedure
1 100 g of chicken manure and 1 litre of distilled water were heated in a water bath to 35 °C, mixed and placed in the container
2 The container was placed in a water-bath at 35 °C
3 The volume of gas produced each hour was measured over a 5 hour period.

TASKS

a Using Pratima's results, plot a line graph of volume of gas produced per hour against time. *(3)*
b From Pratima's results, predict what volume of gas is produced if the investigation is continued for another hour. *(1)*

c The results show that the chicken manure is a better producer of biogas. However, the water content of the materials used differs. Explain how this influences the results. *(2)*

d Other than the water content of the materials used, select *one* other aspect of the procedures which does not allow a fair comparison. *(1)*

e Express as a ratio the difference in the volume of gas produced per hour, during the 5th hour in both investigations. *(1)*

f Predict what would happen if the cotton wool plug was not in position in the container and blockage occurred. *(1)*

g Suggest a reason why rubber tubing must *not* be used in this experimental set up. *(1)*

9 SHELF-LIFE

To extend the shelf-life of food, the food can be sealed in a pack which is filled with a mixture of nitrogen (N_2) and carbon dioxide (CO_2). This excludes air from the pack. Oxygen in the air would allow a faster rate of spoilage, owing to a greater growth rate of microorganisms.

The bar chart shows by how many days the shelf-life of gas-packed vegetable salads are extended, at different temperatures, compared with air-filled controls.

Spoilage in N_2/CO_2 packed salads was found to be due mainly to fermentation by yeast. Fermentation occurs in only oxygen-free, anaerobic conditions, with the formation of various by-products including carbon dioxide.

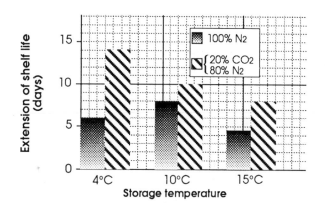

TASKS

a Which gas mixture extends the shelf-life more? *(1)*

b State the relationship between temperature and shelf-life, for the 20 % CO_2/80 % N_2 mixture. *(1)*

c Suggest, with a reason, what changes occur in the mixture of gases in a gas-packed salad, after spoilage starts. *(2)*

d An air-packed salad, stored at 4 °C, starts to spoil after 20 days. What is the percentage increase in the shelf-life at 4 °C if it is packed in a 20 % CO_2/80 % N_2 atmosphere. *(1)*

e An air-packed salad, stored at 10 °C starts to spoil after 10 days. Express, as a ratio, the difference in its storage life and that of a salad, stored at the same temperature in a 20 % CO_2/80 % N_2 atmosphere. *(1)*

10 FUNGI AND ALGAE AS FOOD

Read the passage below and complete the tasks which follow.

Protein is required in the human diet for the formation of new cells, for both growth in size and repair of damaged tissue. Protein also forms enzymes and hormones, which control all body activities. For the majority of the world's population, the
5 food type in greatest shortage is protein. It is with this fact in mind that sources of protein, as alternatives to meat, milk products and eggs, have been sought.

Algae as food.
Algae are simple plants which live in water. Many hundreds of years ago Mexican Indians harvested the alga, Spirulina,
10 from lakes. The algae were dried and provided a protein-rich food. Algae such as Spirulina are being grown again in many areas of the world. Their advantages are that they make organic food through photosynthesis, growth is rapid and they give a high yield when compared to other food sources.
15 Algae are very inexpensive to grow. The yield of Spirulina is 50 000 kilograms per hectare, this is 12.5 times the yield of wheat and 500 times the yield of cattle.

Fungi as food.
Fungi, such as mushrooms, have been eaten for centuries. It is other types of fungi rich in protein, which are now being

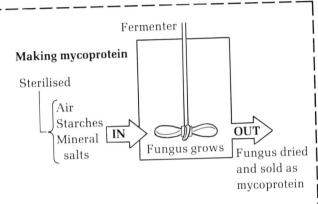

Making mycoprotein

20 developed for human consumption. One such fungus, Fusarium, contains about 45% protein and this compares favourably with meat. It also has a high fibre content which gives bulk and roughage to the diet. A British company, RHM, has developed a method of growing mycoprotein (protein
25 from fungus). Fusarium grows well on a variety of waste starches from wheat or potatoes. The fungus can then be used to make artificial meat, by adding appropriate flavourings. This has a texture which is chewy and similar to meat.

TASKS

a What reasons are given, to explain the need for developing cheap, alternative sources of protein (lines 1–7)? (2)

b Calculate the yield of wheat in kilograms per hectare (line 17). (1)

c Describe briefly how Spirulina could be cultivated on a commercial scale (lines 8–14). (2)

d Select *two* facts about the composition of Fusarium which makes it a good food source (lines 26–28). (2)

e Copy and complete the table below, which compares both methods of protein production (lines 8–26). (4)

Algal production	Fungal production
	Food source waste starches and mineral salts
High yield	
Texture of dried plant material	
	Relatively cheap

Read the passage below and complete the tasks which follow.

A natural hormone that athletes could take illegally to improve performance is now available commercially. It could keep the cheats ahead of scientists trying to catch them
5 out with new methods of detection. Erythropoietin (EPO) is produced chiefly in the kidneys and regulates the production of red blood cells. Athletes could use the commercial version of it to fortify their blood before big
10 events. The artificial version of EPO is indistinguishable from the natural substance and, in theory, is undetectable.
Until recently, scientists could only obtain EPO from human body fluids—and in such
15 small quantities that it would be useless commercially. That has changed thanks to advances in biotechnology. Amgen, a biotechnology company based in Los Angeles, now makes EPO in bulk and sells it under the
20 trade name Epogen.

The drug is meant for patients on renal dialysis who are suffering from severe anaemia. At present, some athletes fortify their blood by removing some of their own, freezing it for
25 storage, and reinjecting it close to an event. The practice-known as blood doping—raises the concentration of red blood cells and the oxygen they carry. However, recipients require a reinfusion of at least one litre of
30 blood, so a doctor has to supervise this type of treatment at all times.
Bo Berglund, an expert on blood doping at the department of internal medicine at the Karolinska Hospital in Stockholm in Sweden,
35 says that individuals wishing to use EPO instead, would simply have to inject it three times a week for six to eight weeks. There is, however, a possibility of acute toxicity with this drug...and it increases the chances of a
40 stroke.

This first appeared in New Scientist

TASKS

a Why is commercially produced erythro-poietin undetectable as a drug (lines 10–12)? *(1)*

b State the function of erythropoietin within the human body (lines 6–8). *(1)*

c Account for the fact that erythropoietin has, only recently, become available as a possible drug for use by athletes (lines 13–20). *(2)*

d State the proper medical use of erythro-poietin. *(1)*

e Describe the process of blood doping (lines 23–26). *(2)*

f Explain the advantages of erythropoietin use to an athlete (lines 26–37). *(3)*

g State *two* dangers associated with the use of high levels of erythropoietin (lines 37–40). *(2)*

12   MYCOTOXINS

Read the passage below and complete the tasks which follow.

DIY KIT WEEDS OUT FOOD TOXINS

A team from a British company is flying to the Far East to demonstrate a do-it-yourself kit for detecting dangerous toxins in foodstuffs. Mycotoxins are poisonous chemicals produced
5 by moulds that grow in a variety of stored crops, particularly maize, peanuts and wheat. One toxin, aflatoxin B, which is produced by the mould *Aspergillus flavus,* is hazardous in the tiniest quantities and has been linked with
10 cancer of the liver. Most countries set limits for levels of contamination and will not import tainted crops. Until now, the only way to detect the toxins has been by chemical analysis which is reliable but takes several days. Bill
15 Stimpson and John Smith, scientists at the University of Strathclyde developed antibodies that pick up aflatoxins. They are sensitive down to two parts per billion. May and Baker Diagnostics of Glasgow, developed and have
20 produced two versions of the test. The first gives a result in five minutes so it is ideal to check a lorry load of grain for example. The second does 40 tests at a time, which means that samples can be taken from throughout a
25 shipment of grain or peanuts and a large quantity can be cleared at once. It takes two hours.
Tainted crops are difficult to sell to countries with strict laws on acceptable levels of toxin,
30 and aflatoxins can cause considerable loss of revenue. The usual way round this problem is to export the high quality crops and sell the poor foodstuffs at home.
Peter Calkin, chairman of Agmmark, is work-
35 ing to develop markets for surplus African produce and is delighted with the kit. It provides a quick and cheap means of quality control. It allows him to check that all the produce he deals with meets the health stand-
40 ards of potential importers. The kits will help to reveal the extent of the problem of aflatoxin contamination. This in turn might perhaps persuade governments of tropical countries to develop better storage facilities or to introduce
45 laws on the sale of contaminated foodstuffs.

Adapted from New Scientist

TASKS

a State the source of mycotoxins (line 4).   (1)
b What danger is associated with afla-toxin B (line 7)?   (1)
c State the chief advantage of the new kit over the previous method used to detect aflatoxins (lines 12–27).   (1)
d What fact suggests that the new kits are very sensitive in detecting aflatoxins?   (1)
e Why is it important that samples are taken *from throughout a shipment* (line 24)?   (1)
f Explain why Third World countries ex-*port the high quality crops* (line 32).   (2)
g What *two* developments does Peter Calkin hope will emerge as the *kits reveal the extent of the problem of aflatoxins* (lines 40–45)?   (2)

Read the passage below and complete the tasks which follow.

Enzyme offers brighter future

Trials start next year on a dipstick which can indicate in just 10 minutes whether or not a patient has a bacterial infection. The doctor dips the stick first into a urine sample and then
5 into a mixture including an enzyme extracted from fireflies. The mixture lights up if the test is positive. It is the latest application of bioluminescence. Such applications will save time, money and lives by early detection of
10 anything from salmonella in packaged food to unwanted yeast in supposedly alcohol-free lager. All living cells use adenosine triphosphate (ATP) to carry energy. If you mix ATP with two compounds extracted from
15 fireflies - luciferin and the enzyme luciferase - the energy given off is directly proportional to the amount of ATP, which shows how many microorganisms were in the original sample. In practice, a sample is mixed with a reagent
20 which degrades any nonmicrobial ATP. Then the ATP which is contained in the bacterial cells is extracted and mixed with the luciferin and luciferase. The light is measured by a luminometer.
25 The food and drink industry is also very interested in ATP because ATP testing makes it easy to check every batch of a product and the results are delivered before the goods leave the factory. Tony Evans of Thames Water believes
30 that "it is more luck than judgment" that a major disaster has not been caused by the delay before bacteriological results are available using culturing. He hopes to develop a two hour water test using ATP assaying.
35 Robert Miller, a microbiologist, carries out routine ATP testing of every batch of Tennent's Export and Barbican before it leaves the Brewery. His research shows that the ATP test will cut the time to detect lactobacilli, the bacteria
40 which cause beer to spoil.

Adapted from New Scientist

TASKS

a What is meant by *bioluminescence* (line 8)? (1)

b What is the main theme of the passage? (1)

c Explain how the reaction causes the mixture to light up *if the test is positive* (lines 6–7). (2)

d Show the shape of the curve in a graph of the amount of light given off and the amount of ATP present (lines 13–18). (1)

e Explain why any *non-microbial ATP* has to be removed before the test is carried out (line 20). (2)

f State the chief advantage of the above test to the food and drink industry (lines 25–29). (1)

g Explain why the test will be of importance to water authorities such as Thames Water (line 29). (1)

h Name the *two* organisms in the passage for which the brewing industry will be testing. (2)

Increasing fruit juice extraction

All plant cells are surrounded by a non-living cell wall made up of various chemicals which include cellulose and pectin. If pectin is removed from the cell wall, the cell wall becomes more permeable. The ability to make the cell wall more permeable is important to fruit juice manufacturers. The more permeable the cell wall, the greater is the yield of juice. An enzyme called pectinase has the ability to digest the pectin of the cell wall. Apple sauce sold in a tin is made from the fruit juice pulp after the apple juice has been extracted.

Craig and Joanna carried out an investigation on the effect, at room temperature, of the enzyme pectinase on the extraction of juice from apple sauce pulp.

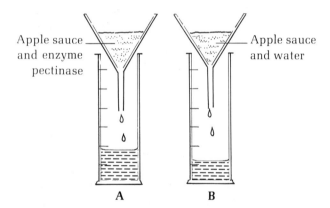

Apple sauce and enzyme pectinase — A

Apple sauce and water — B

Joanna's procedure

1 50 g of apple juice were placed in beakers A and B
2 5 cm³ of a 1 g in 10 cm³ suspension of the enzyme pectinase was added to beaker A
3 5 cm³ of distilled water was added to beaker B as the control experiment
4 Both beakers were stirred and left for 5 minutes to allow the enzyme to act

5 The apple sauces were poured through filter paper as shown
6 The volume of juice being filtered was measured every 5 minutes for 20 minutes.

Results

Time (mins)	Volume of juice extracted (cm³)	
	Apple sauce and pectinase	Apple sauce and distilled water
5	12	3.5
10	20	5.0
15	23	5.5
20	24	6.0

Craig's procedure

1 50 g of apple juice were placed in beakers A and B
2 1 g of pectinase powder was added to beaker A
3 5 cm³ of distilled water was added to beakers A and B
4 Both beakers were stirred and left for 10 minutes to allow the enzyme to act
5 The apple sauces were poured through filter paper as in Joanna's procedure
6 The volume of juice being filtered was measured every 5 minutes for 20 minutes.

Results

Time (mins)	Volume of juice extracted (cm³)	
	Apple sauce and enzyme pectin	Apple sauce and distilled water
5	14	3.5
10	21	5.0
15	24	5.5
20	26	6.0

a What conclusion can be drawn from the results of both procedures? Explain your answer. (2)

b Account for the difference between the two sets of results in Joanna's procedure. (1)

c 1 What *two* aspects of the procedures do not allow a fair comparison of Joanna's and Craig's results? (2)

2 Explain how each aspect brings about the difference in results. (2)

d Using the results from Craig's procedure, construct a bar chart showing the change in the volume of extract produced with time in the experiment and the control. (4)

e Account for the observation that the rate of filtration is greatest over the first 5 minutes. (1)

f Calculate from Craig's results the percentage increase in juice extracted after 20 minutes, caused by the enzyme pectinase. (1)

15

Sugar beet proves resistant to herbicide

Plant scientists in Belgium have grown genetically engineered sugar beet that survives the action of a weedkiller. It is the first time that researchers have managed to grow sugar beet
5 plants from single cells carrying a foreign gene for herbicide resistance. The researchers aim to produce a variety of sugar beet that survives when sprayed with a herbicide that kills weeds. They have inserted into cultured cells of sugar
10 beet a gene taken from the bacterium, Streptomyces. The gene orchestrates the production of an enzyme that deactivates the herbicide. The company used standard techniques for inserting the foreign bacterial gene
15 into sugar beet cells. The Stryptomyces gene is first spliced into a plasmid (gene carrier) of another bacterium, *Agrobacterium tumefaciens*. When *A. tumefaciens* is co-cultured with cells of the sugar beet plant, the plasmid moves from the
20 bacterial cells to the plant cells, carrying the Streptomyces gene with it.

Adapted from New Scientist

TASKS

a Use the words from the passage to complete the description of genetic engineering. The — — — — from Streptomyces which gives — — — — to the herbicide, is cut out from Streptomyces and then — — — — into a plasmid of the bacterium *A. tumefaciens*.
A. tumefaciens is cultured with cells of — — — —. The — — — — from Streptomyces — — — — from the bacterial cell into the plant cell. (3)

b Explain the importance of the fact that the gene is transferred into single, isolated cells of the sugar beet and *not* into some of the cells of a sugar beet plant. (2)

c Describe how the transferred gene allows the variety of sugar beet to be resistant to the herbicide. (1)

d Explain the advantage of this type of genetic engineering to the farmer. (1)

Read the passage below and complete the tasks which follow.

Adapted from New Scientist

FOOD IRRADIATION

Food irradiation is our first alternative to heat as a way of inactivating microorganisms or parasites in food.
Short-wave ionising radiation passes
5 through food carried on a conveyor belt. As it does so, it inactivates or destroys microorganisms without cooking the food (see table).
Fears have been voiced about the safety
10 of irradiated food, in particular that such food would have unacceptably high levels of radioactivity. However, research has shown that irradiation does not significantly increase the natural radioactivity of food.
15 Nor would the technique be used on all foods.
The technique is already being used selectively in many parts of the world. US and USSR space missions use irradiated food.
20 Advantages of food irradiation are that it could improve safety; reduce spoilage; increase the shelf-life of foods and favourably modify the texture of certain foods.
25 Disadvantages of food irradiation are that it reduces the levels of some vitamins, particularly vitamin C and thiamin. Low doses would not usually inactivate enzymes or viruses that cause food to spoil. Nor would
30 irradiation normally render harmless any microbial toxins that are already present in food. The technique would not be used on very oily or fatty foods because it oxidises the fats and results in the food tasting bad.

Dose (kilograms)		Applications
Low	0.20	To kill parasites such as *Trichinella spiralis* and *Taenia saginata* in raw meat
	0.40	To kill insects in cereal grains, fruit, cocoa beans and other crops
	0.60	To inhibit sprouting or germination in certain crops, for example, onions and potatoes
	0.80	To control ripening, for example, tropical fruits
Medium	2.0	To reduce microflora that spoil meat, fish, fruits and vegetables
	8.0	To kill live food-poisoning bacteria, particularly *Salmonella* and *Camylobacter* in raw poultry, prawns and shellfish
High	15.0	To reduce bacterial contamination of herbs and spices

* Irradiation would not be used on all foods. It would complement existing methods of reducing contamination by microorganisms.

TASKS

a Construct a bar chart to show the dosage of irradiation used in the different applications. *(3)*

b Express as a ratio the difference in the dosage of irradiation used to kill food-poisoning bacteria, and insects in cereal grain. *(1)*

c State *one* advantage of irradiation, as a way of inactivating microorganisms or parasites in food, over heat methods (lines 4–7). *(1)*

d What *two* answers are given to allay fears that *food would have unacceptably high levels* of radiation (lines 9–14)? *(2)*

e Explain why irradiated food is used on space missions (line 19). *(2)*

f Using the information from lines 20–34, construct a table comparing *three* advantages with *three* disadvantages of food irradiation. *(3)*

g If food which is no longer fresh is irradiated it can be stored for as long as fresh food. What is the danger to the consumer of this type of practice? *(1)*

17

Read the passage below and complete the tasks which follow.

BIOTECHNOLOGY REAPS REWARD ON TOBACCO ROAD

Gene farmers reaped another victory last week. The US government has given permission to a biotechnology company to grow genetically engineered tobacco plants in a plot in Wisconsin.

5 The test site is surrounded by soyabeans and is about half a kilometre from any other tobacco plants. All but five of the disease-resistant plants will be uprooted before they flower.

The flowering stalks of the five remaining will be 10 covered in bags to ensure that no pollen escapes. Commercial tobacco crops suffer from the bacterial pest, *Agrobacterium tumefaciens*, which attacks any wound on the plant's surface. The bacterium induces the growth of tumours known 15 as the crown gall. *A. tumefaciens* is believed to induce an unusual ratio of plant growth substances including cytokinin, in infected cells. The increase in cytokinins is somehow instrumental in the formation of these galls, which can weigh 20 up to 40 kilograms each.

The novel tobacco plants will be grown from seed into which genes are inserted to replace the cytokinin gene. Therefore, even if the plant becomes infected, it will not be able to produce 25 cytokinin necessary for galls. About 1000 plants altered in this way have been exposed to the bacterium over the past two years, none has become diseased.

Adapted from New Scientist

TASKS

a What is the reason for taking each of the following precautions during the trials on the tobacco?
  1 The test site is half a kilometre from any other tobacco plant (line 6). *(1)*
  2 The flowering stalk of the remaining plants are covered to ensure that no pollen escapes (lines 9–10). *(1)*

b Explain how attacks by *A. tumefaciens* reduce the tobacco yield. *(1)*

c Describe the mechanism by which the genetically engineered tobacco plants overcome invasion by *A. tumefaciens*. *(2)*

d What evidence suggests that the development of tobacco plants which are resistant to *A. tumefaciens* has been a success? *(1)*

GENETIC FINGERS IN THE FORENSIC PIE

A murderer was convicted last week after being identified through genetic fingerprinting. The technique for obtaining a genetic fingerprint is as follows: DNA is extracted from suitable tissue. The DNA extract is subjected to enzymes which chop it into tiny pieces. The pieces are separated in an electric field: the smaller pieces of DNA move faster and further in the electric
5 field than the larger DNA strands. The pieces of DNA are then fixed onto a membrane to retain their relative positions. In the next stage, the DNA is subjected to Jeffreys probes, which identify and label certain strands of DNA. A film is developed in which the DNA probe complexes appear as dark bands (see Fig.I). Professor Jeffreys of Leicester University discovered that the pattern that the strands of DNA produced was unique to the individual - as unique in identification terms
10 as a fingerprint.

In January 1987, Leicestershire Police embarked upon a mass screening exercise to track down the killer of two schoolgirls murdered (3 years apart) in the villages of Enderby and Narborough. Genetic fingerprinting tests were performed on semen samples recovered from the girls' bodies, as forensic evidence and the results clearly showed that because the DNA
15 profiles from these two samples were identical, the same man was responsible for both crimes. The genetic 'manhunt' began and all men in the villages were asked to volunteer a blood sample for testing. Only two men did not give samples one had a genuine reason, the other was the man now convicted of these crimes. Colin Pitchfork attempted to evade the net by persuading a workmate, Ian Kelly, to give a sample in his place. It was only when a work colleague
20 overheard a conversation by Kelly that it all came to light. The police were informed, Pitchfork's arrest followed, and in January 1988 he became the first murderer in the world to be convicted by the power of genetic fingerprinting.

1 2 3   Blood stain

TASKS

a What physical factor is the basis for the separation of DNA fragments in an electric field (line 6)?   (1)

b Why is it important that the DNA strands *retain their relative positions* (line 6)?   (1)

c In paternity cases, what is the significance of each parent having a unique pattern of DNA bands (lines 8–10)?   (2)

d Explain how DNA fingerprinting can be applied to any crime in which biological samples are left at the scene of the crime.   (3)

e Explain how identification of a criminal is possible even when the only sample of the criminal's tissue is mixed with blood from the victim.   (3)

f Suggest a further application of DNA fingerprinting not mentioned in the passage.   (1)

g Part of the pattern of DNA strands from a mother and daughter are shown. Copy the diagram and show those bands which would be present in the father's pattern.   (1)

Mother Daughter

h In the photograph, which of the DNA fingerprints made from the blood samples of three suspects matches the bloodstain found at the scene of the crime?   (1)

19

CITRIC ACID PRODUCTION

The flow chart below outlines the production of citric acid, by submerged fermentation. The spores of the fungus *Aspergillus niger* are passed into the inoculum fermenter which contains molasses (treacle) to which has been
5 added various materials which are essential for fungal growth. When the inoculum mould growth has reached a satisfactory stage and is judged to be free from contamination, it is transferred to the production fermenter.

Uses of Citric Acid

Citric acid occurs in most living cells, but is, perhaps, best
10 known as the acid constituent of citrus fruits. Together with the citrates it is used in a wide variety of foods and medicinal products, as is shown in the table opposite of breakdown of usage in the United Kingdom.

In the soft drinks industry both citric acid and sodium
15 citrate are added to carbonated and non-carbonated drinks where they act as flavour enhancers and help to retain the carbon dioxide. In the health field, citric acid and sodium carbonate are used in effervescing salts to control the formation of excess hydrochloric acid in the stomach.
20 Sodium citrate is used as an anticoagulant wherever blood is handled, as, for example, in the blood transfusion service and in slaughterhouses and meat processing plants. In the confectionery field citric acid is added to sweets, cake fillings and jams as a flavouring but it also
25 plays an important part in the setting of jams and jellies. Finally, citric acid is used in industrial cleaning, as a descaling agent and sodium citrate can be used in the detergent industry as a replacement for phosphates.

Breakdown of usage	% usage
Soft drinks	50.0
Health salts	25.0
Other foods	12.5
Confectionery	10.0
Other uses	2.5

Production of citric acid by Submerged fermentation

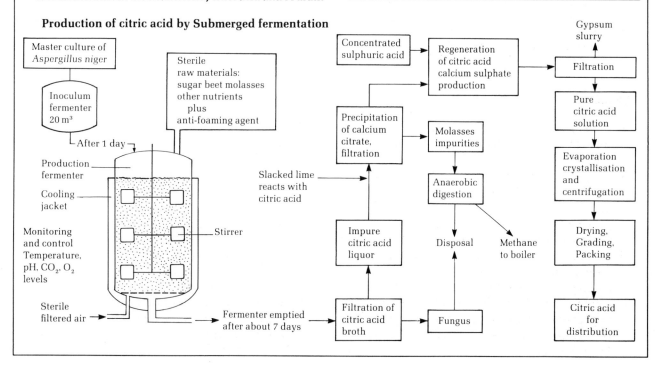

a Explain the benefit of using an *inoculum fermenter* rather than an immediate *inoculation* into the production fermenter. (2)

b Explain the importance of each of the following when using a production fermenter:
   1 monitoring and control of temperature levels (1)
   2 sterile-filtered air. (1)

c From the flow chart:
   1 Select an energy-saving (and thus cost saving) stage (1)
   2 Describe how the impure citric acid liquor is purified for distribution. (3)

d Construct a pie chart, from the data in the text, to show uses of citric acid in the UK. (2)

e Copy and complete the table below. (3)

Industry	Example of usage
Soft drinks	
	Controls level of stomach acid
Blood transfusion	
Confectionery	

20

Knowledge on the growth of bacterial populations helps to improve the efficiency of biotechnological production processes. Bacteria can reproduce by binary fission, in which a single bacterium divides into two identical offspring.

Time (hours)	Number of bacteria (thousands per mm³)
5	0.20
10	0.60
15	1.15
20	1.75
25	2.55
30	3.30
35	4.00
40	4.60
45	5.10
50	5.40
55	5.50
60	5.50

The table shows the number of bacteria growing in a nutrient broth at 30 °C, over a period of time.

TASKS

a Plot a line graph to show the change in bacterial numbers with time. (3)

b From the graph, how many bacteria/mm³ are present in the broth 44 hours after the start of the investigation? (1)

c During which 10 hour period is the growth in numbers of bacteria greatest? (1)

d How many hours does it take for the population of bacteria, present after 5 hours, to increase 20 times? (1)

e What evidence supports the statement that after 60 hours the numbers of bacteria being produced by binary fission is balanced by the numbers dying? (1)

APPENDIX

The following serial numbers for food additives may be used in the ingredients
lists on food labels as alternatives to their names.

COLOURS

E100	Curcumin
E101	Riboflavin **(Lactoflavin)**
101(a)	Riboflavin-5'-phosphate
E102	Tartrazine
E104	Quinoline Yellow
107	Yellow 2G
E110	Sunset Yellow FCF **(Orange Yellow S)**
E120	Cochineal **(Carmine of Cochineal or Carminic acid)**
E122	Carmoisine **(Azorubine)**
E123	Amaranth
E124	Ponceau 4R **(Cochineal Red A)**
E127	Erythrosine BS
128	Red 2G
E131	Patent Blue V
E132	Indigo Carmine **(Indigotine)**
133	Brilliant Blue FCF
E140	Chlorophyll
E141	Copper complexes of chlorophyll and chlorophyllins
E142	Green S **(Acid Brilliant Green BS or Lissamine Green)**
E150	Caramel
E151	Black PN **(Brilliant Black BN)**
E153	Carbon Black **(Vegetable Carbon)**
154	Brown FK
155	Brown HT **(Chocolate Brown HT)**
E160(a)	alpha-carotene, beta-carotene, gamma-carotene
E160(b)	annatto, bixin, norbixin
E160(c)	capsanthin **(Capsorubin)**
E160(d)	lycopene
E160(e)	beta-apo-8'-carotenal (C_{30})
E160(f)	ethyl ester of beta-apo-8'-carotenoic acid (C_{30})
E161(a)	Flavoxanthin
E161(b)	Lutein
E161(c)	Cryptoxanthin
E161(d)	Rubixanthin
E161(e)	Violaxanthin
E161(f)	Rhodoxanthin
E161(g)	Canthaxanthin
E162	Beetroot Red **(Betanin)**
E163	Anthocyanins
E170	Calcium carbonate
E171	Titanium dioxide
E172	Iron oxides, iron hydroxides
E173	Aluminium
E174	Silver
E175	Gold
E180	Pigment Rubine **(Lithol Rubine BK)**

PRESERVATIVES

E200	Sorbic acid
E201	Sodium sorbate
E202	Potassium sorbate
E203	Calcium sorbate
E210	Benzoic acid
E211	Sodium benzoate
E212	Potassium benzoate
E213	Calcium benzoate
E214	Ethyl 4-hydroxybenzoate **(Ethyl *para*-hydroxybenzoate)**
E215	Ethyl 4-hydroxybenzoate, sodium salt **(Sodium ethyl *para*-hydroxybenzoate)**
E216	Propyl 4-hydroxybenzoate **(Propyl *para*-hydroxybenzoate)**
E217	Propyl 4-hydroxybenzoate, sodium salt **(Sodium propyl *para*-hydroxybenzoate)**
E218	Methyl 4-hydroxybenzoate **(Methyl *para*-hydroxybenzoate)**
E219	Methyl 4-hydroxybenzoate, sodium salt **(Sodium methyl *para*-hydroxybenzoate)**
E220	Sulphur dioxide
E221	Sodium sulphite
E222	Sodium hydrogen sulphite **(Sodium bisulphite)**
E223	Sodium metabisulphite
E224	Potassium metabisulphite
E226	Calcium sulphite
E227	Calcium hydrogen sulphite **(Calcium bisulphite)**
E230	Biphenyl **(Diphenyl)**
E231	2-Hydroxybiphenyl **(Orthophenylphenol)**
E232	Sodium biphenyl-2-yl oxide **(Sodium orthophenylphenate)**
E233	2-(Thiazol-4-yl) benzimidazole **(Thiabendazole)**
234	Nisin
E239	Hexamine

	(Hexamethylenetetramine)
E249	Potassium nitrite
E250	Sodium nitrite
E251	Sodium nitrate
E252	Potassium nitrate
E260	Acetic acid
E261	Potassium acetate
E262	Sodium hydrogen diacetate
262	Sodium acetate
E263	Calcium acetate
E270	Lactic acid
E280	Propionic acid
E281	Sodium propionate
E282	Calcium propionate
E283	Potassium propionate
E290	Carbon dioxide
296	DL-Malic acid, L-Malic acid
297	Fumaric acid

ANTIOXIDANTS

E300	L-Ascorbic acid
E301	Sodium L-ascorbate
E302	Calcium L-ascorbate
E304	6-*O*-Palmitoyl-L-ascorbic acid **(Ascorbyl palmitate)**
E306	Extracts of natural origin rich in tocopherols
E307	Synthetic *alpha*-tocopherol
E308	Synthetic *gamma*-tocopherol
E309	Synthetic *delta*-tocopherol
E310	Propyl gallate
E311	Octyl gallate
E312	Dodecyl gallate
E320	Butylated hydroxyanisole **(BHA)**
E321	Butylated hydroxytoluene **(BHT)**
E322	Lecithins
E325	Sodium lactate
E326	Potassium lactate
E327	Calcium lactate
E330	Citric acid
E331	Sodium dihydrogen citrate **(*mono*Sodium citrate)**, *di*Sodium citrate, *tri*Sodium citrate
E332	Potassium dihydrogen citrate **(*mono*Potassium citrate)**, *tri*Potassium citrate
E333	*mono*Calcium citrate, *di*Calcium citrate, *tri*Calcium citrate
E334	L-(+)-Tartaric acid

E335	monoSodium L-(+)-tartrate, diSodium L-(+)-tartrate
E336	monoPotassium L-(+)-tartrate **(Cream of tartar)**, diPotassium L-(+)-tartrate
E337	Potassium sodium L-(+)-tartrate
E338	Orthophosphoric acid **(Phosphoric acid)**
E339	Sodium dihydrogen orthophosphate, diSodium hydrogen orthophosphate, triSodium orthophosphate
E340	Potassium dihydrogen orthophosphate, diPotassium hydrogen orthophosphate, triPotassium orthophosphate
E341	Calcium tetrahydrogen diorthophosphate, Calcium hydrogen orthophosphate, triCalcium diorthophosphate
350	Sodium malate, sodium hydrogen malate
351	Potassium malate
352	Calcium malate, calcium hydrogen malate
353	Metatartaric acid
355	Adipic acid
363	Succinic acid
370	1,4-Heptonolactone
375	Nicotinic acid
380	triAmmonium citrate
381	Ammonium ferric citrate
385	Calcium disodium ethylenediamine NNN'N' tetra-acetate **(Calcium disodium EDTA)**

EMULSIFIERS, STABILIZERS, THICKENERS AND GELLING AGENTS

E400	Alginic acid
E401	Sodium alginate
E402	Potassium alginate
E403	Ammonium alginate
E404	Calcium alginate
E405	Propane-1,2-diol alginate **(Propylene glycol alginate)**
E406	Agar
E407	Carrageenan
E410	Locust bean gum **(Carob gum)**
E412	Guar gum
E413	Tragacanth
E414	Gum arabic **(Acacia)**
E415	Xanthan gum
416	Karaya gum
E420	Sorbitol, sorbitol syrup
E421	Mannitol
E422	Glycerol
430	Polyoxyethylene (8) stearate
431	Polyoxyethylene (40) stearate
432	Polyoxythylene (20) sorbitan monolaurate **(Polysorbate 20)**
433	Polyoxyethylene (20) sorbitan mono-oleate **(Polysorbate 80)**
434	Polyoxyethylene (20) sorbitan monopalmitate **(Polysorbate 40)**
435	Polyoxyethylene (20) sorbitan monostearate **(Polysorbate 60)**
436	Polyoxyethylene (20) sorbitan tristearate **(Polysorbate 65)**
E440(a)	Pectin
E440(b)	Amidated pectin
442	Ammonium phosphatides
E450(a)	diSodium dihydrogen diphosphate, triSodium diphosphate, tetraSodium diphosphate, tetraPotassium diphosphate
E450(b)	pentaSodium triphosphate, pentaPotassium triphosphate
E450(c)	Sodium polyphosphates, Potassium polyphosphates
E460	Microcrystalline cellulose Alpha-cellulose **(Powdered cellulose)**
E461	Methylcellulose
E463	Hydroxypropylcellulose
E464	Hydroxypropylmethylcellulose
E465	Ethylmethylcellulose
E466	Carboxymethylcellulose, sodium salt **(CMC)**
E470	Sodium, potassium and calcium salts of fatty acids
E471	Mono- and di-glycerides of fatty acids
E472(a)	Acetic acid esters of mono- and di-glycerides of fatty acids
E472(b)	Lactic acid esters of mono- and di-glycerides of fatty acids **(Lactoglycerides)**
E472(c)	Citric acid esters of mono- and di-glycerides of fatty acids **(Citroglycerides)**
E472(e)	Mono- and diacetyltartaric acid esters of mono- and di-glycerides of fatty acids
E473	Sucrose esters of fatty acids
E474	Sucroglycerides
E475	Polyglycerol esters of fatty acids
476	Polyglycerol esters of polycondensed fatty acids of castor oil **(Polyglycerol polyricinoleate)**
E477	Propane-1,2-diol esters of fatty acids
478	Lactylated fatty acid esters of glycerol and propane-1,2-diol
E481	Sodium stearoyl-2-lactylate
E482	Calcium stearoyl-2-lactylate
E483	Stearyl tartrate
491	Sorbitan monostearate
492	Sorbitan tristearate
493	Sorbitan monolaurate
494	Sorbitan mono-oleate
495	Sorbitan monopalmitate